Psychology
in Nursing

MODERN PRACTICAL NURSING SERIES

This important nursing series, designed for the Pupil Nurse, is
published as a 'parent' book covering the basic skills entitled AN
OUTLINE OF BASIC NURSING CARE, and a number of smaller
handbooks covering the individual specialities as the nurse is moved
from one discipline to another.

Modern Practical Nursing Series

16

Psychology in Nursing

John Sugden S.R.N., R.M.N., R.N.T.,
Lecturer in Nursing Studies
Queen Margaret College; Edinburgh

WILLIAM HEINEMANN MEDICAL BOOKS LIMITED:
LONDON

For Julie and Sarah

First published 1975
© John Sugden 1975
ISBN 0 433 31900 3

Typeset by H Charlesworth & Co Ltd, Huddersfield
Printed and bound in Great Britain by
Redwood Burn Limited, Trowbridge & Esher

Contents

Introduction

There is no psychology which is relevant only to one section of the community. The aim of this book is therefore to outline some of the situations and their solutions, which any person near to hospital patients will recognize and think about. Whenever possible the text is related directly to the people in these situations and for that reason it largely avoids what has come to be known as 'psychological jargon'.

The ideas expressed in this book come from a host of colleagues and friends in nursing and allied professions with whom I have worked, talked and learned over the years.

The term 'nurse' is used to denote any person, male or female, involved in the daily nursing care of the patient.

March 1974

1
The Nature of Psychology

Biology is the science which studies living organisms. Its subdivisions deal with different aspects of the organisms.

1 Anatomy is concerned with the structure
2 Physiology is concerned with function — the ways by which the organism works
3 Psychology is concerned with behaviour and a simple definition of psychology is — 'the study of behaviour'.

Just as nurses and others caring for the sick study anatomy and physiology, so should they be concerned with the psychological aspects of the patient's illness.

Aims of Psychology

The principle aim of psychology is to discover, and to be able to describe, the environmental and biological basis of human behaviour and thus to further an understanding of ourselves and those around us. In hospital, where the patient's psychological reactions greatly influence his illness, this is especially important.

Methods of Psychology

The aims of psychology may be pursued in a number of ways and methods. The ways in which we study behaviour in hospitals are twofold:

1 The Naturalistic Method
This aims at the observation of behaviour in natural surroundings and without the interference of the observer.

Hence a nurse may make observations, sometimes of a subjective nature, about a patient's reactions to being in hospital for example. Observations such as these are really of limited value if not augmented by other methods.

2 The Clinical Method

This is used to 'diagnose' behaviour in the individual. The immediate aim of this method is practical – ie to help the patient.

In gathering such information, or data, standard psychological tests, histories, and social reports – such as domestic environment are used. Clinical evaluations and the application of psychological tests is the function of a clinical psychologist. A clinical psychologist is therefore a graduate psychologist who has specialized in clinical psychology (ie psychology of sickness) and differs from a psychiatrist in that he is not a doctor of medicine who has specialized in treating mentally sick patients.

BEHAVIOUR

The study of behaviour is in itself sub divided into various sub categories. In studying psychology a nurse is primarily concerned with human behaviour but may find it necessary to refer to data from animal experiments which sometimes have application to human behaviour.

FACTORS GOVERNING BEHAVIOUR

1 An Innate or Inborn Factor

This is the constitution with which we are endowed with, by the passage of chromosomal material from parents to offspring. Thence we are compelled to do and behave (along a general line) as human beings do. We cannot fly or burrow in the ground because we are not equipped (constitutionally) to do so. These factors are not normally adaptable since they depend upon physiological and anatomical entities!

2 Experience

Our behaviour is modified by our experiences, eg we know that if we plunge a hand into a fire or into very hot water, we will be burned. We will therefore not repeat such an experience. Although this is a fairly concrete example, behaviour may be modified by experiences which we cannot recall. This is an important point in how behaviour is governed throughout life.

3 Culture Pattern

We are born to a certain way of life, that is, to a pattern which varies from country to country; from county to county; and even from town to town. This way of life to which we are born is a product of hundreds of years of development and observation of different cultures indicates different behaviour patterns.

4 Teaching and Learning

This is conscious and deliberate. We learn for ourselves and consciously set about the business of learning.

Behaviour at any level results from reaction to stimulus.

A stimulus in psychology means anything that reacts as an organism. The stimulus is not the force which makes us behave as we do but might be described as the trigger which fires the gun. The organism itself selects the reaction.

TYPES OF BEHAVIOUR

Reflexes or Reflex Action

A reflex is a direct muscular or glandular response to a sensory stimulus and is the lowest form of behaviour in man. Reflexes are usually simple involuntary actions which are inborn in all human beings. They are performed automatically and sometimes quite unconsciously in response to certain stimuli:

eg Jumping at a pin prick
   Blinking at a bright light
   Sneezing when the nose is irritated
   Jerking the lower limb when the patella tendon is tapped.

These are muscular responses which are sometimes used by the doctor when he examines the integrity of the nervous system. There are also glandular responses:

The salivary glands secrete saliva in response to the taste of food. The lachrymal glands (tear glands) discharge tears when the eye is irritated.

A true reflex has certain characteristics. For example, it is a reaction to a direct physical stimulus and operates through the spinal cord without being first referred to the brain. The response is immediate and is involuntary and unconscious. Reflexes are not acquired but there may be slight variations in them in illness. A fact which a doctor makes use of in diagnosis of certain physical conditions. Finally, reflexes are universal to the species, all men have a certain number of specific reflexes.

Conditioned Reflexes

Most reflex responses can be aroused not only by a natural stimulus (unconditioned) but also by any stimulus with which the natural stimulus has been constantly associated. (Conditioned stimulus). This fact has been well demonstrated by Pavlov's experiments which were mainly concerned with salivary reflexes in dogs. He made a small incision in the cheek of his experimental dogs and drew out one of the salivary ducts. By attaching a rubber tube, it was then possible to collect and measure precisely the saliva produced. The natural, unconditioned stimulus to salivation is food in the mouth. What Pavlov discovered was that if some other stimulus eg a bell rang or a light flashed immediately before or together with food, the dog soon learned to associate the bell or light with food and consequently salivated on the appearance of the signal even when no food was produced. This secondary stimulus is the conditioned reflex. The conditioned reflex may also be called:

Conditioned response
or conditional reaction
or associated reflex.

4

Instincts

A psychologist called McDougall has defined instincts as an inherited or innate psycho-physical disposition which determines its possessor to perceive and pay attention to objects of a certain class, to experience an emotional excitement of a particular quality upon perceiving such an object and to react in regard to it in a particular manner or at least to experience an impulse to such action!

Instinctive behaviour has four characteristic features:

1 The performance of complex trains of activity, engaging the whole organism which
2 are of biological value to the species
3 are similarly performed by all members or sexes of the species
4 do not have to be learned. They are performed perfectly (or at least adequately) at the first attempt.

With instinctive behaviour there is no external stimulus. The 'drive' is within the organism ie there is no goal.

DIRECTED BEHAVIOUR

The mechanism of this form of behaviour is not fully understood, the goal is probably unknown. This fact can be illustrated by observing the ritualistic behaviour of certain animal species which cannot modify the pattern of behaviour which is carried out instinctively. The behaviour pattern is a rigid one.

In higher animals such as man the pattern of purposive, unlearned behaviour becomes less rigid. The higher animals are endowed with intelligence and as this endowment increases up the biological scale, so does the capacity to adapt behaviour. The ends can be achieved despite some changes in the environment. The emphasis changes from the actual behaviour, to the drive or instinct behind the behaviour. Moreover with human beings, not only the means to the goal but the goal itself is adaptable. On this process of re-direction (or sublimation) depends art, science, civilization and all the highest achievements of humanity.

In human beings therefore, there is nothing that is done instinctively, but there are Innate Drives which cause us to act in a fixed manner. There is a modern tendency to use 'instincts' when referring to animals and 'drives' in relation to man.

McDougall used the term 'propensity' instead of instincts which meant the same thing applied to human beings, he implied 'instincts' as being animal.

PRINCIPAL HUMAN INSTINCTS

Many psychologists have attempted to list and to classify the human instincts. Unfortunately no two give exactly the same list. But there are seven fundamental tendencies which would be acceptable to nearly all psychologists.

The seven instincts, drives or propensities or pretendencies are:

1 Food seeking (Nutrition)
2 Curiosity
3 Fear
4 Aggression
5 Self Assertion
6 Maternalism (Paternalism)
7 Acquisitiveness.

Some psychologists add to this list:

Gregariousness, the herd instinct, (a tendency to group with other human beings), and
Constructiveness — a tendency to construct things.

All these display the characteristics of instinctive behaviour as outlined previously.

EMOTIONS

With the development of the instincts there is also the development of feeling states which we call emotions. All (cognitive) thinking processes are accompanied by certain conditions of consciousness

6

called 'affects'. In current usage, affects are any kind of feeling or 'emotion' attached to ideas. These affects are usually due to the interaction between the individual and his environment.

Feelings

These are states which develop with relatively mild interactions of low intensity and usually of short duration.

Emotions

These are more complicated and are distinguished by physiological changes which accompany them. These changes are associated with the autonomic nervous system and include

- rapidity of the heart rate
- increased respiratory rates
- sweating and so on. . .

These effects being due to the release of adrenaline. Emotions are generally attached to objects, situations or people. They are of relatively high intensity and of long duration.

Moods

These are dispositions to experience of a certain type of emotion in a particular point in time. Like emotions they are of relatively long duration and high intensity.

Sentiments

These systems of emotional dispositions centre around an object.

Attitudes

In these the emphasis is not emotional but more intellectual and is not related to specific objects but groups of objects, subjects etc such as religion, politics, etc. Attitudes are usually shaped in childhood, re-examined during adolescence, and hardened in adult life.

Interests

Here the emphasis is even more intellectual and remoter still from emotion.

7

TEMPERAMENTS

Temperaments are the general set of the individual's personality to adopt certain types of sentiments and is more or less characteristic of the individual. Many psychologists relate temperament to body build or physique. This probably originates from the ancient world where scholars described four types of individual which can almost be related to a modern technique of relating personality to body build. These were:

Sanguine

People in whom blood predominates giving the individual a hopeful, courageous, confident   disposition.

Melancholic

People in whom 'Black bile' predominates, driving the individual a tendency towards depression and ill-found fears.

Phlegmatic

People in whom the 'phlegm' predominates giving a rise to coolness, sluggishness and apathy.

Cholergic

People in whom yellow bile predominates giving the tendency towards anger.

The modern classification is somewhat similar and will be mentioned later.

Physiological Manifestations of Emotions

Some physiological manifestations of emotion are evident in everyday life and in addition can be readily detected by examination of blood and urine or by the use of 'Sphymamanometer' and cardiograph. These physical observations which are frequently used to monitor a patient's progress can therefore be influenced by emotional situations.

In 'emotion provoking' situations a variety of physiological changes take place. Emotion involves the whole of the nervous system but some parts of the nervous system are more intimately involved.

Origin of Emotions

The first attempts to define and study emotions were, like many other psychological studies, undertaken by philosophers who regarded emotions as being inborn. They also suggested that emotions were responsible for all our actions and they described some fifty of them.

In modern times the major work on emotions has been undertaken by a physiologist called Shand.

Shand suggests that there are in fact only four emotions from which there are derived secondary emotions. The four primary emotions are:

1 Joy
2 Sorrow
3 Fear
4 Anger.

McDougall whom we referred to in speaking of instincts, defined seven emotions (related doubtlessly to the instincts) and coupled them with propensities which he said these emotions called out in the individual:

Emotion	Propensity
Fear	Flight
Wonder	Curiosity
Anger	Aggression
Disgust	Repulsion
Tender emotion	Protection
Subjection	Submission
Positive self-feeling	Self assertion.

He described a secondary emotion as being a combination of two or more of the above.

Developmental Theory of Emotions

Most psychologists would probably subscribe to the view that at birth the infant is completely devoid of emotion. (Since you will recall, emotions 'develop' as a result of inter-actions with the environment). But there develops what has been called a generalized feeling of excitement which then develops into the emotions which we have defined. This generalized excitement continues throughout life.

This idea therefore suggests, that the capacity to be emotional is inborn in everyone whilst the emotions themselves are learned. The way in which the generalized excitement differentiates as a result of learning is illustrated thus:

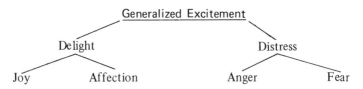

From the above diagram we could therefore say that the moment of birth the newborn has only one variety of 'emotional' response namely the generalized excitement which takes place whenever bodily changes or stimulation takes place. Thus the first intense bodily sensations which take place associated with the processes of eating and eliminations lead to the generation of the generalized excitement. As the infant develops he gradually increases the range of his emotions and begins to develop specific emotional reactions. The most profound of these reactions are

1 Affection
2 Anger

Affection is associated with suckling of the mother's breast and satiation of hunger drives. Anger is associated with the frustration of desire and deprivation of satisfaction. Anger in babies quickly changes to affection when the frustrated desire is satisfied.

During early life the child has almost no control over his

emotional reactions and the intensity of his outbursts is extreme and may fluctuate in intensity from emotion to emotion.

As the child begins to learn to manipulate and to control his environment the intensity and frequency of his emotional outbursts tends to decrease. At the same time objects and situations which have not previously aroused emotion through a process of 'conditioning', often come to do so eg fear of the dark, fear of animals and so on.

Sometime after the age of five years, children develop a fairly high degree of control over their emotions. The situation being helped by the parent's training of the child. In our society a child is also expected as time goes on to learn to accept frustrations and disappointments. He gradually develops a decreasing dependency on his parents and of his mother especially.

Later, when he is older still, a large part of his emotional development is influenced by people outside his family as he finds confidence and security in group associations.

The period of adolescence is characterized by swinging moods, self-consciousness, intense emotional strain, criticism of parents and defiance of those in authority. This is a natural and transient process and represents the last stage of 'weaning' the child from his dependence on his parents.

Emotional Maturity

A normal man on reaching adulthood is at the peak of his physical, psychological and therefore emotional development.

This situation is necessary in order that he be able to meet the standards of society and to accept responsibility at work, in marriage and parenthood.

Emotion as a Factor in Disease

The symptoms resulting from fear or anxiety include:

1 Tremor
2 Palpitations

3 Frequency of mictuition
4 In severe cases, complete collapse.

These are produced by the emotions, through stimulation of the autonomic nervous system and the endocrine glands such as the adrenals, pituitary and thyroid. There is recognition of the fact that emotional distress may play a part or contribute to the development of organic diseases such as gastric ulcer, skin diseases, colitis, etc. This participation of psychology mechanisms into physical illness has developed into a special branch of medicine called psychosomatic medicine.

BEHAVIOUR OF THE PATIENT IN HOSPITAL

As we have seen from the preceding material, behaviour is a term used to describe all human activity both innate and acquired.

Behaviour which is seen in hospital may be normal or abnormal.

Behaviour which is abnormal ie a symptom of illness, is usually called pathological behaviour or sometimes symptomatic behaviour. Much of the patient's behaviour however is normal in as much as it is a normal reaction to a particular situation. For example, if a patient becomes emotional when told he is seriously ill, then his reaction is normal because it is appropriate to the situation.

In observing the patient a nurse may indeed be required to observe signs of abnormal behaviour. The primary task, however, is to observe and interpret the patient's 'normal' reactions and modify negative reactions to be positive and hence salutiferous.

Abnormal Behaviour

Behaviour is a response to a stimulus. This statement implies that without a stimulus a response cannot take place. In certain situations, however, the patient may respond to 'stimuli' which are either not present or which are the wrong stimuli for the particular response.

All behaviour requires a specific sequence of events related to the central nervous system.

The cerebral cortex is the centre of the brain which integrates perceptual experiences (awareness of objects, persons or situations via the five senses). The response is formulated into wilful movement via the mid brain and spinal cord, thus it is the brain's function to deal with stimuli received from the environment.

In certain physical illnesses, emotional situations, and mental illness the integrity of the brain is jeopardized. The patient may thus have perceptual experiences of a false or inappropriate nature.

Perception, the way in which we make contact with the environment via the five senses, gives rise to what are called sensations. To perceive an object is to think of it with the aid of sensory facilities, therefore perception is a sensation and its meaning is supplied by the mind. The process is influenced to some degree or other by:

The direction of our attentions

Expectations which we have of the sensation

Desire

It is much easier to find a book on a shelf if we know what it looks like than if we merely know the title. On the other hand when the condition of the 'expectant' attention prevails or the patient is in a highly emotional state then every square shape will be thought to be the badly wanted book and we may have disordered perception in the form of illusions.

Illusions

An illusion is a false perception, where the stimulus results in an act of perception but the mind (ie the brain) reads a different meaning to it. In other words they are misinterpretations of stimuli and it may be:

1 Auditary
2 Gustatory
3 Olfactary
4 Tactile
5 Visual

Illusions may be caused by:

1 Physical factors, eg a mirror image
2 Mental pre-occupations or anxiety, eg ghosts
3 A response to insufficient data eg sensation of movement which are experiences in a stationary train when one beside it moves off
4 Drugs and toxic poisons causing perplexity eg a patient with uraemia or vitamin B deficiency
5 Expectant attention, explained above.

In the normal person, illusions are quickly dispelled and corrected by use of reasoning power and by further investigation, but in the mentally ill they form part of conditions such as psychosis, hysteria and epilepsy.

Hallucinations

These are false perceptions for which there is no stimulus. They have the vividness of real experiences and affect the subject in exactly the same way. Hallucinations are classified according to the sense involved in the same manner as illusions.
Some causes of hallucinations are:

1 Mental ill-health
2 Fatigue
3 Drugs and toxic substances (eg alcohol)
4 Hypnosis.

Normal people suffer from a mild form of hallucination which is called a hypnogogic hallucination. Hypnogogic hallucinations occur on the point of going to sleep. The mentally ill person suffering from hallucinations responds to them in a way that to him is normal, rational and 'the only way'. But his response is not considered normal by others of the same social status or education. The differences between illusion and hallucinations are illustrated on page 15.

Illusions	Hallucinations
All of us may experience them	Few of us experience them
Have clear external stimulus	No external stimulus
The same situation arouses the same sensation in all of us	Those hallucinated in the same circumstances have different hallucinations.

Belief

Belief is an attitude involving the recognition or acceptance of something real. Sometimes beliefs are disordered and the effects of the situation is to distort the patient's interactions with others and often to create inappropriate abnormal behaviour.

Delusions

These false beliefs that do not alter despite appeals to reason and logic and which are out of keeping with the patient's backgrounds, race, culture and educational experiences.

A false belief in itself does not constitute a delusion. It arises from imperfect knowledge or reasoning and it is possible to rectify it by explanation or further examination.

A delusion on the other hand is not susceptible to proof or argument and is held in spite of the clearest evidence of its mistaken nature. In some cases, the nature of the delusion can only be recognized by comparing it with former convictions but the person suffering from delusions needs no proof in support of it. To him his own certainty is sufficient.

Delusions may develop gradually as an outcome of existing depression eg delusions of unworthiness. Less frequently they arise suddenly in connection with illusions and hallucinations in mental illness.

In certain cases of mental illness delusions are dependent one upon the other and a primary morbid belief results in the gradual growth of a number of secondary delusions. Thus a delusion of suspicion may gradually give rise to a delusion of persecution and this in turn to a delusion of grandeur. These delusions are said to be 'systematic' or 'systematized' ie delusions related to one and other.

An 'unsystematized' delusion is one that is not consistent with the patient's general behaviour, eg a patient states that he has no stomach, yet enjoys eating.

Delusions may also be 'fixed' ie one which the patient retains throughout his illness or they may be 'fleeting' ie one which the patient gives up in exchange for another.

MENTAL MECHANISMS

Mental mechanisms are irrational modes of thought which greatly influence behaviour. They may be regarded as inferior or immature solutions to conflicts or difficulties. Mental mechanisms are often used in situations which either:

Create anxiety

or

Threaten or cause loss of esteem.

It is, therefore, not surprising that they are widely operative in the hospital environment both amongst patients and staff. Practically no one can really survive in a psychological sense without their use at sometime. They are not necessarily held to be pathological.

One or other of the mechanisms may predominate in any given type of situation which produces conflict or anxiety but some or even all of these modes of thought play a part in every-day mental activity.

Mental mechanisms secure an individual's adaptation through an attempt to resolve:

Intrapsychic conflicts between parts of oneself.
Extrapsychic conflicts between oneself and the external environment, and are in fact defensive operations of the 'ego' designed to avoid mental suffering or discomfort.

Sublimation

This is the mechanism when an impulse conflicts with internal or external forces and cannot be directly satisfied, it can often find a substitute satisfaction by being re-directed into intellectual activity or artistic creation. The process by which the unsatisfied impulses are re-directed in valuable activities is called 'sublimation' and is considered to be the best possible method of dealing with mental conflict and frustration.

It is in other words diversion of tendencies from prohibited channels to other channels which are socially permissible.

Repression

When an impulse which has to be restrained and controlled because of moral code or social convention cannot be successfully sublimated, it may undergo 'repression'.

It is the thrusting out or the suppression of rising into consciousness of painful ideas.

It is a wholly undesirable way of dealing with an unwelcomed tendency by refusing to admit its existence in order to evade mental conflict.

If a sentiment is repressed, it becomes a 'complex' and considerably influences behaviour.

The successful handling of children depends to a large extent on encouraging sublimation rather than repression eg playing football rather than smashing windows. The aim should be never to forbid a child to do anything without providing an alternative which would be regarded by the child as an improvement on the original intention.

Projection

This is an unconscious mental mechanism by which painful ideas are disowned and attributed to other people. In this way we may be prone to be over-critical to the faults of others from which we ourselves suffer.

This mechanism has been made use of in projection tests where we interpret the situations by reading into them our own experiences and feelings. Hallucinations and delusions are morbid ideas projected by the patient on to his environment.

In hospital, relatives of patients who die or who are very ill may project feelings of guilt onto the hospital and suggest that the hospital's incompetence is in some way responsible for the patient's illness.

Over-Compensation

This is an attempt to make up for a defect of which we are well aware by over-development of some other quality, eg aggressive behaviour may be an over-compensation for shyness. Sometimes in hospitals, older male patients may behave immodestly to over-compensate for feelings of sexual inferiority which the incapacity of their illness has produced.

Regression

This is an unconscious retreat to an earlier or more primitive stage of development or form of behaviour, eg childish emotionality which is seen in immature individuals, bed-wetting in disturbed children. Many hospitals encourage the use of the regression mechanism albeit unconsciously because it enables adult patients to be looked after by young people in esteem-losing situations. Note how many patients become concerned about bowel movements and eating. Both activities being associated with infantile satisfactions. Children regress when a younger sibling comes on the scene to rival them and they may behave like a baby demanding to be fed, cuddled and so on.

Dissociation

This is a partial or total kind of dis-organization of personality when, under intolerable strain, it splits off or dissociates into segments.

These two or more parts may behave as though they were un-related and function independently. In this way the conflicting tendencies are satisfied alternately, but never allowed to enter consciousness together. Through this mechanism, a person unconsciously refuses to recognize certain unpleasant items in his life, eg may forget this portion of his life.

Dissociation occurs in varying degrees from minor moral lapses to the complete dissociation which occurs in some neurotic disorders such as fugue states and multiple personality. The most famous case of multiple personality was 'Eve' who was the subject of the film 'The Three Faces of Eve'.

Fugue is a form of automatism during which a person wanders or undertakes some journey. The projection of ideas which occurs in delusional states is a form of dissociation.

Denial

Denial is the situation where the individual 'denies' an unpleasant situation exists. The denial is on a conscious level. Unconsciously the individual is aware of the reality.

CONCEPTS AND PROCESSES OF THE MIND

We are all aware that there is in our mind much more than is present in consciousness at any given moment.

There are many ideas, memories and urges lying just beyond the threshold of awareness ready to emerge at the beckoning of a conscious wish or in response to a relevant stimulus. They may have been on the other hand, thrust so far below consciousness that they cannot normally rise again to the surface.

The idea of these preconscious and unconscious memories, emotions and urges may be at first difficult to grasp but it is essentially for understanding the aspects of normal and abnormal behaviour.

According to Sigmund Freud the mind is stratisfied into three layers:

1 Conscious

This level consists of those mental processes of which a person is aware with varying degrees of distinctness at any given time.

2 Preconscious (or subconscious)

Levels containing memories which although they are not in full consciousness are not repressed and are easily recalled to consciousness.

3 Unconscious

This is the result of the mental mechanism repression and contains mental elements incompatible with the conscious mind. These ideas and urges and memories most often come into conflict with the standards of morality, ethics or aesthetics and cannot be normally recalled to the consciousness.

The mind therefore can be compared to an iceberg; the conscious is the visible part, while the unconscious is submerged and greatly exceed the conscious part.

The contents of unconsciousness is primitive, animal and selfish in its aims. It consists of mass of inherited instinctive impulses, the 'id' which is a power-house of mental apparatus and is at variance with conscious thoughts, the 'ego' and especially with ideas of morality, the 'super-ego'.

'Ego' is a product of development and represents adaptation of inherited instincts to environment. After maturation it becomes a dynamic centre of behaviour integrating, compromising and solution forming.

'Super-ego' (the Censor) represents incorporation of parental moral, attitudes determined by existing cultural standards into restrictive, permissive or standard setting internal forces of personality. Primitive thoughts and wishes as well as emotional reactions do not dissolve completely at maturation, but remain latent in the 'unconscious' which defends itself by the existence of a barrier or 'censor' acting through the mechanism of 'repression'. Anything that conflicts with our conscious thoughts becomes repressed into unconscious and cannot, owing to 'censor' take part in conscious mental processes except by roundabout methods in disguised form, such as dreams, symptoms of mental disorders, forgetting, states of dissociation or automatism. Between the conscious and unconscious is the stratum or 'pre-conscious' containing matter which is only partially repressed as well as an abundance of fairly recent experiences.

Co-ordinated, rational behaviour can be maintained only through constant struggle of ego's, 'reality principle' against tendencies for immediate gratification displayed by 'Id'.

Dreams

From the psychological point of view sleep is a periodic withdrawal from reality and suspension of interest in environment. The conscious level of the mind is almost entirely out of action, and hence the unconscious tends to assert itself, and is usually successful in evading the vigilance of the censor. The work of the unconscious finds expression in dreams.

Dreams have been described as 'the royal road to the interpretations of unconsciousness' and Freud called them 'the guardians of sleep'. They provide one of the commonest outlets for tendencies that are repressed or unsatisfied in waking life. Thus tension generated by repression is released.

The 'manifest content' of a dream is the dream as related by the dreamer soon after waking. To each dream there is hidden meaning known as the 'latent content'. The 'dream-work' is the process by which the latent content is transformed into the manifest content.

The dream-work follows certain principles or mechanisms of which the most important are:

1 Symbolisation

This substitutes symbols for the wishes repressed in the unconscious mind. It occurs mostly in adults, as childrens' dreams are direct undisguised fulfilment of wishes.

2 Condensation

This is where a single 'dream-symbol' stands for two or more ideas, events or persons.

3 Displacement (of affect or emphasis)

Where important content of the dream may turn out to be trivial when investigated and that which appears insignificant may have important value.

4 Dramatisation

The dream represents a drama in which the people are representing (as they do on the stage) certain ideas of mind, and not the people themselves. The dream thoughts are arranged here in such a way as to form a play which may be acted sometimes in a bizarre way, leading to further concealment of the true meaning.

Dramatization is allied to symbolism, because conflicts and tensions in the mind of the dreamer are externalized and made more vivid eg an attack of conscience may be represented as an attack by enemies or confronting a difficulty such as climbing a mountain. Dreams are usually quickly forgotten which is a sign of resistance to the disclosure of unconscious wishes.

OTHER FACTORS WHICH INFLUENCE BEHAVIOUR

There are numerous other factors which influence the patients' behaviour; many of which will be discussed in other parts of the book. Three other factors will be examined here. They are:

1 Personality
2 Intelligence
3 Learning.

Personality

'Personality' is all those unique characteristics of an individual by which others identify him. It consists of integration of an individual's physical structures, modes of behaviour, interests, attitudes and abilities.

We are characterized or distinguished from others by our personality, but only those aspects of us and of our behaviour which are more or less permanent are really characteristic and these are 'personality traits' eg emotionality, dominance, sociability, etc. These personality traits, rather than personality as a whole can be measured by tests of personality which a clinical psychologist may use to assess difficulties in these respects. Many people tend to think of personality as some sort of desirable outgoing type of behaviour and we see patients as having 'pleasant' or 'unpleasant' personalities. What this really means is that certain traits in individual patients' personalities may be unappealing to us. A patient's personality therefore directly influences our inter-actions with him since it influences his behaviour.

Character

This is a personality viewed from an ethical or moral point of view and our most enduring characteristics which have social and moral significance are referred to as 'character traits' eg honesty. Therefore 'personality' refers to behaviour which may be favourable or unfavourable while character refers rather to conduct which may be right or wrong.

Temperament

Our physical appearance is also important because it determines to a large degree how others react to us which in turn also determines our reactions to them. If we are avoided for example, because of our behaviour or appearance, we may respond by becoming aggressive or by withdrawing from contact with others.

In the past, psychologists have attempted to type individuals in terms of physique in order to claim that each physical type of character by a certain type of personality.

Amongst the psychologists who have attempted such a classification are Jung and Kretchner.

Jung based his typing into 'extroverts' and 'introverts', on intellectual functioning or attitudes of mind. The extrovert is cheerful, sociable, optimistic, impulsive and subject to mood swings but basically practical minded.

The introvert on the other hand is cool and deliberate, who thinks before he acts. He is a poor mixer, preferring his own company to that of others.

Kretchmer's types were based upon the physical appearance of the individual and included:

1 Pyknic

   who was a thickset stocky person subject to mood swings and running into fat in later life.

2 Asthenic

   who was pale, tall, narrow chested with a humourless, unsocial personality and who generally preferred his own company.

3 Athletic

   who was a big boned muscular person with a stable temperament.

THE ORIGIN AND GROWTH OF PERSONALITY

Personality being intimately related to the physical organism exists from time of conception. Differences in appearance and behaviour are already apparent at birth, but sufficient learning and maturation to form distinctive habits of adjustment ie 'personality traits' do not come before the fourth month of life and definite adaptive responses to the physical environment and people before the second half of the first year of life.

This does not mean to imply that personality traits are definitely fixed in early childhood. Variations in social stimulation, illnesses, accidents and other incidents may lead to a marked and unpredictable change in personality traits. We may think of development of personality therefore as being a result of two general influences:

1 The biological endowment

2 The environmental experiences.

The biological influence is represented most clearly through the effect of secretions from the endocrine glands on physique and temperament and through the role of the nervous system on acquisition of personality traits. Injuries to the brain, senility, infection or toxaemias of one sort or another, often lead to marked changes in personality.

The environmental or situational influences begin soon after birth as we are again being thrown into one social situation after another each of which may leave its imprint upon our personality.

Our personal consistency will depend upon:

1 The culture in which we develop
2 The kind of parents, teachers, work-mates or marriage partners we have
3 Our socio-economic status and measure of prestige.

MAIN DEVELOPMENTAL PERIODS OF PERSONALITY FORMATION

Infancy	Up to two years	Dependency upon parents
	three to six years	Effects of illness, jealousy, parental disharmony etc
Late childhood	six to twelve years	Social adjustment difficulties
Adolescence	Twelve to eighteen years	Period of emancipation with complexities of sexual and social development. Possible anti-authority phases and delinquency
Constructive period	Seventeen to twenty years	Clarification of philosophical and religious concepts and thinking becomes abstract and discriminative
Maturity	Twenty years +	Self control and reliance.

ASSESSMENT OF PERSONALITY

To assess someone's personality is to know that particular person well enough to be able to compare him with other already known persons.

Personality may be investigated by various tests (methods) which are of value in indicating:

1 The general pattern of psychological activity within a personality as a whole
2 The presence of particular traits not apparent to clinical examination or not evident on verbal examination or interview

These tests of personality are usefully used together with intelligence tests to reveal attitudes and interests which can indicate the directions in which the patient can best express himself and use his intellectual capacity.

The main personality tests are of the 'projection' type. That is, when the patient is presented with an ambiguous stimuli they evoke in him imaginative responses which can be 'scored' to reveal his basic personality traits. Therefore, what an individual 'projects' is believed to indicate certain hidden or concealed factors in his personality.

INTELLIGENCE

Intelligence is one of those terms with which almost everyone is familiar, but which almost no-one can adequately define. Some psychologists have actually called it 'that which is measured by intelligence tests' !!

It is an abstract term which certainly indicates to a great extent an individual's performance on standard tests but which might be defined something like the following:

'Intelligence is the ability of an individual to respond to and to modify his environment in order to profit by his experience, to store and utilize knowledge.'

In individuals there is a great deal of variation in intelligence. In the same individual, intelligence alters with age, being at a peak round about 16 years and beginning to deteriorate as early as the twenties. It is likely that intelligence is an inherited potential but its growth and development is profoundly altered by factors such as disease, injury or unfavourable environments such as those without intellectual stimulation of emotional security.

Even an ideal environment, however, helps little when the potential for normal development is poor.

Intelligence can be measured on standardized tests which are treated statistically. These tests are so constructed as to measure not what a person has learned but his capacity to learn.

The intelligence of an individual undoubtedly effects his response to situation. A more intelligent individual is likely to be able to understand, for example, that certain restrictions may be placed upon him when he is ill. He will doubtless comprehend any reasonable instructions or explanation which is given to him. On the other hand a less intelligent patient may be unable to comprehend its nature and restrictions, that his illness necessitates. Not being able to understand is likely to effect his emotional state to some degree or other.

Mental Age

In order to make comparison with individuals of different ages, vast scores on intelligence tests are expressed in terms of mental age.

It is an average age at which a random group of children would be as intelligent as the particular child who is tested.

Intelligence Quotient

The score in most intelligence tests is expressed as 'intelligence quotient' and is based upon the relationship between a chronological age ie the calendar age and the mental age. It is then multiplied by one hundred to express it as a percentage.

$$\text{Intelligence Quotient} \quad = \quad \frac{\text{Mental Age} \times 100}{\text{Chronological Age}}$$

The average intelligence quotient is between 90 and 110 and the population as a whole conform to the curve of normal distribution. The number of people whose intelligence deviates from normal on average therefore, decreases at either end of the scale, eg

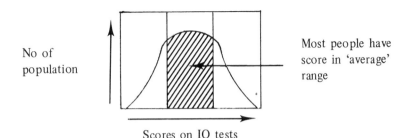

No of population

Most people have score in 'average' range

Scores on IQ tests

Normal Curve of Distribution – Intelligence

Whilst the mental age of a child increases during the period of bodily growth, the ratio of mental age over chronological age remains approximately constant. It is this constancy of intelligence quotient which gives intelligence tests their predictive value.

The chief values in determining a child's intelligence quotient are that:

1 Those with a low IQ may be selected for special education or training which is within the limits of their capacity
2 Vocational guidance can perhaps be more wisely given if a child's IQ is known.

Intelligence Testing

Is not merely a procedure devised to enable an examiner to calculate the IQ which is of secondary importance; the real value is that it is an interview with the individual being tested.

The techniques of testing are standardized to obtain not merely information, in isolation at the testing situation, but in perspective, allowing comparisons, child with child, age with age and abnormality with abnormality. The undue attachment of importance to IQ is unfair to the individual being tested since various conditions such as nervousness, shyness, or tiredness at the time of the examination may result in poor performance. It is wise therefore to base opinion not on pure IQ, but rather on a general impression obtained by the clinical psychologist at the time of testing.

The IQ can be determined at an early age using what are called 'developmental inventories' rather than IQ tests.

Intelligence Tests

Tests are standardized to age and are mainly vocabulary and individual.

They were first used around about 1908. Performance tests are a little different from 'intelligence tests' since they measure specifically performance. Performance tests are therefore tests which call for minimal understanding and use of language. In many of these tests the answers to the problem does not require speech and instructions may be given by, for example, demonstration.

Performance tests measure fundamental psychological processes, such as re-assuring and seeing relationships without at the same time depending upon particular cultural or educational opportunities. They are of particular value with individuals who:

1 Are too young to have learned language
2 Are illiterate through lack of educational opportunities or mental incapacity
3 Cannot or will not speak
4 Can only speak a foreign language.

Performance tests require minimal degree of verbal ability and can be administered to individuals ranging in age from infancy to the adult level.

2
Hospitals

Hospitals of one sort or another, have existed since time immemorial. They are places where sick people go to receive care and treatment which otherwise might not be available to them.

Within this broad definition, each hospital is within itself a particular environment. This environment of course varies with the type of work undertaken in it, with the geographical location, and, more particularly, with the people who work and are treated and cared for within its walls.

To the people who work there the hospital soon becomes an interesting and stimulating environment and, although they may have entered the hospital with misconceived ideas, these are soon put to rights by experience. A process of adjustment takes place over a period of time and ill-founded fears are replaced ultimately in those who remain, by confidence and self-reliance. Each and every day in hospitals people are meeting life crises and inter-personal dramas are being enacted in the hospital wards and departments during every hour of the day.

To a lay person being admitted as a patient to hospital, the situation is a terrifying prospect. They are removed from their normal environment. When anyone is removed from his normal environment he becomes a little anxious. If he is then confronted with an environment which is foreign and about which so many people profess to know so much, if he has ideas about the prospect of hospitalization superimposed upon his fears about his illness, his anxiety is multiplied greatly. The average person therefore arrives at hospital frightened and anxious.

Numerous factors influence his reactions. If he is profoundly ill and the possibility or prospect of dying is real or imaginary in his mind, he may present himself with apparent readiness to submit to whatever is deemed necessary. This anxiety, however, remains. Experience of hospitals, perhaps of a relative or friend's hospitalization, will have a direct bearing. This, of course, may be good or bad since his relative may not have had the best care possible. At any moment in time the media are usually discussing or dramatizing some aspect of hospital life and the wrong ideas of what hospitals should be may be created. Hospitals not living up to this 'ideal' may then be thought wanting in some way.

The most profound, most lasting and most far-reaching influence upon the patient is the situation which is created by those with whom he interacts on a face to face basis. The hospital staff, their behaviour, attitudes and effectiveness are, therefore, the single most important influence upon the patient. Environments, generally speaking, are a product of the people within them. A hospital environment may, therefore, be 'good' or 'bad' according to the kinds of psychological support and care afforded to the patient. The functions of a hospital are therefore two-fold:

1 That it gives to the patient the best care and treatment to resolve his illness whenever possible
2 That it carries out this function whilst ensuring that *all* the patient's basic needs, both physical and psychological are met.

3
The Nurses

Nurses are people who are trained to care for the sick. Whilst training to be nurses, nursing students and pupils are usually addressed as nurse. For the purposes of this section therefore, the title refers to all those hospital workers who care for the nursing needs of the patient.

No other member of the hospital staff has the same prolonged contact with the patients as do the nurses. It might be said then, that whatever the nurse does and says, the attitudes she displays — indeed the sum total of her daily interactions with her patients are one of the most important factors affecting the patients' psychological well being in hospital.

These daily face to face interactions between nurse and patient, are the basis of the nurse/patient relationship.

Nurse/Patient Relationship

Within the scope of nursing, there are many differing types of task and speciality. Each of these requires perhaps a different type of skill or even personality. For example, a nurse who is especially skilful in dealing with children may not be so adept at dealing with adult or aged patients. An excellent surgical nurse may be a very poor psychiatric nurse.

By and large, the speciality towards which one moves, is to some degree determined by personality factors.

In previous sections we have discussed personality traits and indicated how these may affect relationships with others. Aside from these, there are numerous other 'forces' at work which make our interactions with patients either good, bad or indifferent.

These include:

1 Personal qualities
2 Education and experience
3 The nature of the patient's illness
4 The 'dynamics' of the situation
5 The moods and attitudes of the nurse.

Personal Qualities

It is not possible to define exactly how the best potential can be developed in relationship to specific qualities. However, certain qualities may reasonably be thought desirable. These are as follows:

1 Maturity

A 'mature' individual is one who has developed within herself the compromise between the desires from within herself and the wishes and needs of the society which she inhabits. She is

capable of making reasoned judgments from which she is capable
of taking decisions without being unduly influenced by what people
think about her. Her behaviour is usually stable in that she does
not occupy any extreme position and is capable of responding
to the reasonable argument and opinion of others. A mature
individual does not make excessive use of mental mechanisms and
can tolerate disappointment, grief and daily difficulties with
equanimity. A mature person is self reliant. All people at some
period exhibit 'immature' behaviour. That maturity is desirable in
a nurse seems to be beyond discussion.

2 Perceptiveness to the needs of others

To be able to effectively care for people, to anticipate their
needs in situations where communications are distorted or otherwise difficult, requires a high degree of perceptiveness to the
needs of others. The nurse needs to be able to understand what it
is a distressed, inarticulate patient is trying to get over. Further-
more, she needs to anticipate situations during their incubation
period in order that action may be taken to 'short circuit' the
distress which might be involved. She needs therefore to be
sensitive to the basic human needs of the individual and to be
able to sympathise with the patient.

3 Initiative

There are very many situations in hospitals wherein the nurse
is required to use her initiative. She needs to take action which
left undone, might have profound consequences for her patients.
To act with foresight and to act with assurance are part and
parcel of this.

There are, of course, other personal characteristics which are
important. All these characteristics dictate to a large extent how
she is able to interact. An immature individual cannot for example
be very reassuring to the patient. One without perceptiveness may
create frustration because needs will be left unmet. Without
initiative the nurse will not take it upon herself to fulfil the roll in
which most patients have cast her.

Education and Experience

We are all familiar with the regard in which some nurse training hospitals are held. Equally, we are all aware that some hospitals are concerned with expediency rather than sound nursing education. Many nurses enter the profession with a good education behind them, whilst others enter with minimal educational background. The acquisition of formal education is of course always desirable. It is not necessarily the main criterion for success as a nurse. A sound or unsound nursing education is the real manufacturer of good nurses.

If the education of the nurse has been comprehensive and has included a development of the awareness of a patient's psychological needs, and if efforts have been made to help the nurse understand the need for good personal relationships, then caring for the patient is of the nature of a logical sequence. If the education has felt these things to be of secondary importance, the process does not evolve spontaneously.

We all react to situations which we have encountered previously in a more reasonable way at the second encounter. A nurse with experience of real life situations will therefore find it easier to develop relationships. An older woman with children of her own will find it easy to meet the needs of children. To a great extent, if the nurse has experienced adequate, satisfying, inter-personal relationships of her own, she will be more effective in developing them with her patients. To this extent many situations can be dealt with by 'common sense' measures. These measures are always a result of learning be it intentional or unintentional. Greater confidence comes with experience. One only has to observe the first tentative interactions of a junior nurse when she comes into contact with a patient for the first time. Compare this with the inter-personal skills of an experienced Ward Sister.

The Nature of the Patient's Illness

There are undoubtedly some illnesses in which a patient's perceptions or reality are disordered. There are many physical conditions where the disturbance of body chemistry disturbs the normal functioning and the reasoning and judgment of the patient's mind.

In these situations communications are distorted, gestures are misinterpreted and small mischances are magnified out of all proportion for the unfortunate patient. Not only do these physical symptoms unbalance the equilibrium but so do many psychological symptoms.

In moments of anger or fear we all react sometimes with due process of thought. When we are anxious we constantly look for signs of support and reassurance in others. When these are not forthcoming we are apt, at the very least to be disappointed and at the most openly hostile. All face to face interactions must be 'tested' at first contact. The patient's appreciation of reality is to be established. This must be done unfortunately on a rule of thumb basis, but at the same time with due intellectual process.

Interactions with people are sometimes difficult to begin. If there is evidence that some difficulty is present, it may produce a tendency to withdraw from the patient or to encourage the patient to use unhealthy mechanisms to deal with his problems. It is also true to say that in some situations nurses use the same mechanisms to help them eg both patient and nurse may use the mechanism of 'denial' to deal with the imminent death of a patient. This way both 'survive' even if in an unhealthy manner.

The 'Dynamics' of Nurse Patient Interactions

In all normal situations in which people interact on a face to face basis, there is a natural tendency to move toward a state of social balance. We unconsciously moderate and control our behaviour to maintain this balance eg if two people meet socially and one is especially quiet, it falls upon the other to be a little more talkative or outgoing than normal. On the other hand, if one person is 'excited' and a little over exuberant, the social partner adopts a more submissive role. If this were not so, in many situations, the interacting would either break down completely (both being very quiet for example) or would be chaotic (both being over excited).

In abnormal situations such as those which may be encountered in hospital, the behaviour of the participants may be so profound that normal social equilibrium does not exist. This creates the state of affairs in which the nurse must modify her behaviour in order to recreate a 'normal' situation. If she fails to do so the social balance continues to be disturbed and results in frustration and tension in the participants. She therefore often unconsciously adopts what are in effect restorative forms of behaviour. Examples might include:

Anxiety	— calm
Sadness	— happiness
Inhibition	— forthrightness
Tension	— relaxation

Situations

'Situations' are incidents which occur in the course of the nurse/patient encounters. They usually involve some action or behaviour which is inappropriate. Every situation has time, place and volume. It happens at a particular moment in a particular place and has volume or depth which is relative to the involvement of the people taking part. Within these 'situations' or incidents which take place there are various forces at work. These forces may be either positive or negative.

1 Positive forces are those which are healthy interactions
2 Negative forces are those which are unhealthy because they fail to solve problems and usually create tensions.

The task of a nurse within these situations is to substitute positive forces for negative ones whenever it is possible. They are in a position to do this being the 'healthy' part of the interaction. Sometimes this interjection of a positive force into a situation is a result of unconscious reaction to it. The nurse reacts in a specific way because it seems immediately appropriate. On most occasions, however, it requires a conscious effort by a process of reasoning and

logic. Healthy interactions between the nurse and patient are therefore a result of thinking and reasoning and not of 'common sense'.

Examples:

1 Negative Forces

A patient in hospital has been told he is going to die in a short
time. The patient 'denies' the situation — ie uses a mental
mechanism which denies the existence of the problem — he does
not believe it is true. He may suggest a mistake has been made or
something similar. Into this situation comes a nurse. Knowing
that the patient is using a mental mechanism and therefore solving
conflict in an immature way, she also 'denies' the situation.
Because it is easier to meet the patient face to face whilst denying
the fact of his imminent decease.

2 Positive Forces

A similar situation might be dealt with in a positive manner,
viz:

The patient is told he is dying and he 'denies' the fact is true.
The nurse comes into the situation and helps him to come to
terms with the reality of his condition by confirming what the
doctor has told him, whilst offering subjective support to the
patient.

Other examples of 'situations' and the forces within them are
less concrete than that example. The forces acting upon the
situation are more subtle and hence require more careful
examination. The process of interaction which we have discussed
so far might be described then as having two aspects. That is:

1 The tendency of behaviour to move towards a state of
social equilibrium.
2 'Situations' within which there are positive and negative
forces.

In the nurse/patient relationship, there are two tasks related to
these aspects. These are:

1 Moving in a direction opposite to that of the patient to
create equilibrium where necessary

2 Enabling the patient to utilise or derive benefit from
positive forces which are directed or interjected by the nurse.

TYPE OF INTERACTION

In situations or circumstances where people interact upon a face
to face basis there is a third aspect.   This aspect is the type of
interaction which takes place. Interactions might be:

1 Positive
2 Negative
3 Neutral

Positive interactions include such actions as:

1 Acting upon the other person's suggestions
2 Listening to his advice
3 Offering advice and help whenever it is sought.

It also has regard for the other person's feelings, emotions and
self esteem.

Negative interactions reject suggestion and advice without
thought or consideration. They withhold help and use coersion and
punishment to achieve ends.

Neutral interactions fall somewhere between the two in as much
as the actions would consider the thoughts and advice of the other
person. They would persuade rather than coerce and would consider
the esteem of the other person.

During her daily interactions with the patients, the nurse must be
either positive or at least neutral in her actions.

Other Factors

Some psychologists consider behaviour as being a straight
forward response of an individual which is the result of a definite
stimulus. B. F. Skinner described an extension of this situation
wherein the individual having reacted to a stimulus is rewarded for
his response. The occurrence and frequency of these rewards
increases the likelihood of the particular response being repeated,

ie the individual acting in the same way again. If, however, this reward (or reinforcer) is withdrawn subsequently the frequency of the response on behaviour diminishes and ultimately, unrewarded, is extinguished. Hence behaviour is thought to be a response to a stimulus which is then reinforced.

The stimuli for particular pieces or behaviour (response) are derived directly from the environment as are the rewards. Behaviour therefore, can be controlled by manipulating the stimuli and even better the reinforcers. These facts can be utilized by the nurse to help her change the direction of the patient's behaviour.

Example: The writer witnessed the following example:

A child in hospital was in the habit of head-banging whenever his mother appeared. Being distressed at the sight of the child banging his head his mother would immediately rush up and cuddle and hug him. In effect she was rewarding him for his head banging activity and, therefore, increasing its frequency.

When the facts were examined with his mother and she was advised to cease 'rewarding' his head banging, the activity diminished in frequency and ultimately ceased ie was extinguished.

In her daily contact with her patients the nurse should attempt to terminate inappropriate behaviour by removing the 'reinforcers' and by 'rewarding' behaviour which is socially acceptable and appropriate. It is worth noting that some forms of behaviour may be felt 'acceptable' yet are inappropriate because they are not healthy ways of reacting.

4
Patients

When a person is admitted to hospital, his sensitivities are in no way diminished. Indeed with the exception of special categories of patients his sensitivities are usually greatly heightened as a result of anxiety. The patient therefore has different categories of needs. These include:

1 Biological needs —
   The need of food, warmth and protection.
2 Specific needs related to his illness —
   The need to be 'treated' promptly and efficiently to eliminate his illness.
3 Psychological needs —

Psychological Needs

These are the specific subject matter of this section. Their fulfilment is the nature of an adequate nurse/patient relationship. They include:

1 The Need for Security

This is related to the biological need of protection. Just as the patient who is rendered helpless by physical symptoms required a physical protection, ie if he is paralyzed he needs to be protected from dangers such as hot radiators, fires etc. More specifically the patient is more vulnerable to psychological insecurity, eg he is afraid and often bewildered by his illness.

'Security' also involves freedom from worry about such matters as his family's financial position or his economic status due to his illness. The most important element of psychological security is social security — this is not in a legislative sense, but a 'socialising' sense. We all have a desire to be in a secure environment, to be amongst friends who we believe accept and are concerned about us. We desire and expect 'group acceptance'.

In a social psychological sense it is possible to define this group as two or more people who interact on a face to face basis. Everyone belongs to a number of 'groups'.

In hospital the patient forms part of a group of people with common needs within a hospital ward. Within this wider group small groups form. For example, a group of people having had

surgery might loosely form because they have a common bond.
Imagine a patient within such a group who, instead of being accepted,
was rejected by those with whom he felt a common bond. The
patient would suffer loss of self-esteem because of his rejection. His
'security need' would therefore be unfulfilled and he would generate
anxiety.

To be accepted by the group the patient needs to be able to make
a contribution to it. Other members of the group need to listen to
his advice and accept it when reasonable, to react to his humour and
value his opinions and hospitality. Thus being accepted the patient
requires to know that he is accepted.

2 The Need for Affection

We all require friendship and understanding. In many situations
we require assistance, especially when we feel helpless. Patients in
hospital are especially in need of affection and yet so many are in
situations where it is difficult to give it to them, eg

1 The average person is 'repelled' by a patient with a skin
  condition
2 A patient who is disfigured or mutilated by an accident or
  operation is not usually the patient the nurse spends most time
  being with
3 Some patients who suffer from mental illness exhibit forms of
  behaviour which are distasteful to the average person.

3 The Need for Independence

Babies exhibit the need for freedom from about eight months.
Generally, however, we learn to adapt to limitations on our freedom
due to education and training. Despite this, everyone desires some
form of freedom. In adult life the need is met by placing a person
in a position of responsibility. Most people positively seek
responsibility. Those who do not have usually never had the
opportunity to act independently in childhood.

In hospital by the very nature of the situation, we surrender our
independence and responsibility. We are often in situations where
young nurses 'young enough to be my daughter' are solely

responsible for the patient. Most adults are able to adjust effectively to this situation. Others use the mechanism of regression to diminish the need (or are encouraged to do so). In reality the situation causes a limited disturbance because we think of the situation as 'temporary', ie we surrender independence in order to be treated as a sick person. Nurses can help to make the process easier by treating adult patients as adult patients and interacting on a level high enough to allow the patient a degree of independence. This usually involves using certain phrases when giving instructions. For example, the nurse should not tell a patient to go and have a bath but say, 'would you like to have a bath now?' This type of approach suggests to the patient that the choice is his although it seldom is!

4 The Need to Exercise Initiative

We need to have the opportunity to participate in the environment in terms of being able to criticise, question, observe and so on. A patient in hospital who seeks to discuss his illness is not merely curious about it. He is participating in the 'closed shop' of medical and nursing personnel. He needs to have his questions answered rather than be fobbed off with remarks such as 'you really wouldn't understand'. Because of the type of intimacy to which doctors and nurses are exposed, and because both professions are ethically required to keep private much personal information, nurses find the disclosure of answering of patients' questions frankly very difficult. Between these four psychological needs there is much inter-relation. Deprivation of one affects all of the others. All are essential for happiness and fulfilment. In hospitals, nurses have the prime responsibility for fulfilling them.

SOME PROBLEMS OF NURSE/PATIENT INTERACTIONS

In order to fulfil the patient's psychological needs, the nurse needs to ask herself several questions, viz:

1 How can I help the patient?
2 Am I doing the best for him in psychological terms?
3 Am I sensitive to what the patient is feeling?

4 Are the restrictions which I impose necessary and what to they mean to the patient?

5 Is my relationship with the patient superficial, adequate or am I getting too involved?

The most important point which the nurse needs to grasp is that these needs are not met without conscious effort. They do not respond to unthinking solutions. They require an intellectual process. The first part of this process is to be clear about certain things which we ought to achieve. We define certain goals. These goals are both specific and general.

General Goals

General goals (or objectives) are those which do not necessarily fulfil a specifically defined need. For example, we might say that:

1 A general goal was to help patient when he was in an emotionally stressful situation caused by his illness

2 Another may be to help the patient come to terms with the immediate and perhaps long term effects of his illness

Specific Goals

In defining specific objectives in order to fulfil psychological needs the nurse needs to examine and state specific ways in which:

1 She can help the patient to participate more easily

2 She can make communication easier for him

3 She can increase the patient's self-esteem and thereby his independence.

Participation requires that the nurse examines ways in which he might participate in his treatment and perhaps about the ward generally. She must appreciate the uniqueness of each individual patient and the way in which he might cope with his feelings and anxieties. The whole process requires evaluation of the patient's over-all capabilities, whether he is strong enough in emotional terms to participate in his hospitalization.

A nurse should, of course, always be ready to utilize and respond to the patient's desire to engage in ward activities.

Communication is facilitated by the elimination of technical jargon whilst interacting with the patient. It is helped by enabling the patients to communicate together so that the common bond which exists between them becomes a source of security. Patients will make needs known on a group basis more frequently than individually.

To increase the patient's self-esteem involves making the patient feel worthwhile in situations where he feels hopeless. It is necessary sometimes to re-educate the patient who, for example, has lost a limb or become disfigured, into believing in himself again. It is a difficult and arduous duty.

Moods, Symptoms and Attitudes

In daily life there is a fluctuation in mood day by day. Some days everything is sunshine and on some others it is all cloud. These fluctuations are normal. In hospitals they sometimes become exaggerated so that rather than being moderate daily variations or moods are so profound as to be pathological. When this happens they are important enough to influence the course of the patient's illness.

Some variations in normal reactions or moods include:

1 Aggressiveness
2 Withdrawal
3 Anxiety
4 Sadness
5 Loss of appetite
6 Disturbance of sleep.

Aggressiveness

When confronted with aggressive behaviour from the patient the nurse experiences fear and anxiety.

Fear is when we are afraid of something or someone that we can see and point at, ie something tangible.

Anxiety is when we feel uneasy or in dread about something which we cannot specify. It is usually difficult to distinguish between them in most situations. There are many processes which contribute to the nurse's fears which are derived from different sources:

1 Her own preconceptions, expectations and feelings
2 The activities and attitudes of the group with which she works
3 The attitudes and activities of the patients with whom she works.

Even though a nurse may not have ever seen a particular patient she may be afraid of him. It may be that the patient's 'reputation' has reached her before she has reached him. She has, therefore, got preconceptions that he is something to be afraid of. Generally, realization of one's preconceptions may help to relieve the nurse of her fears and reduce her fears of the patient. In addition very often expectations of situations may play an important part in bringing this about. When a patient who is irritable or aggressive is approached with fear, this often seems to stimulate their aggression. The nurse may also be worried about what other members of the nursing staff feel about her inability to cope with the situation. She asks herself:

1 Whether she will lose her temper
2 Why others can handle the situation when she can't?
   All people are reluctant to admit to their fellows that they are afraid.

If the nurse has specific expectations about the patient even though she has never met him, she anticipates a certain type of response from him.

In most cases when patients have achieved 'reputations' these have usually arisen from small incidents which have happened related to a particular situation. He does not really deserve his reputation. Never the less because of his behaviour, because of his aggressiveness in the past, conveyed from person to person, is the belief he will behave in the same way again.

The patient is aggressive, the nurse instead of recognizing her fears and the patient's desperation, responds with hostility. This reinforces the patient's need to be aggressive which, in turn, reinforces the nurse's need to be restrictive and punishing. This situation disturbs any relationship before it has a chance to develop. The nurse can help solve the problem by:

1 Identifying and being aware of preconceptions
2 Finding out how she came by them, eg
   (a)   Other people's reports
   (b)   Her own experiences
3 Deciding whether her feelings are based upon one incident or a number of incidents
4 Asking whether she is the only one in the ward who is afraid of the patient − if so, why others are not
5 Finding out the reasons for the patient's behaviour; when and with whom he is aggressive
6 Establishing with whom the patient is rarely aggressive, finding out why and then using that model of relationship to develop herself.

The patient may be aggressive for numerous reasons:

1 He may have feelings and attitudes about life and people generally. In this case his hostility is not directed towards the nurse personally. She merely represents a tangible target
2 The patient's illness
3 His desperation in a situation to which he sees no solution
4 A distortion of perceptive experiences
5 A reaction to a situation from which he has no escape; all contribute to feelings of hostility
6 More particularly, he may just be angry or he may dislike the nurse because of her attitudes to him
7 He may suffer impulses which are beyond his control
8 He may be disorientated or merely be behaving in a particular way in order to attract attention to his need of security.

All these reasons may not be readily obvious and only come to light on examination of the problem.

The hostility may be cut short if:

1 The nurse is genuinely interested in helping her patient
2 She is able to examine her own reactions and feelings
3 She is able to reduce the patient's fears and able to restore his self esteem
4 She is able to focus upon the relationship not her fears and positively set about meeting the patient's covert or obvious needs.

WITHDRAWAL

An aggressive patient is one who is usually well known to everyone. It is almost impossible not to acknowledge his disturbance since he comes towards the nursing staff and others. A withdrawn patient is one who stays away from contact and who is frequently overlooked because he is 'no bother'.

1 He is usually quiet
2 He keeps himself to himself
3 He is reluctant to speak
4 His withdrawal is an attempt to solve his psychological problems resulting from his illness by not interacting
5 He is preoccupied with his own problems and yet is unable to solve them with the nurse
6 He is denying himself some of his most important needs
7 He is unable to correct some of his misinterpretations of others because they are due to his physical symptoms acting on his mind.

Many patients are shy, reserved people by nature and they may feel uncertain and uncomfortable with others. In hospital where there is a 'communal living' in the ward, these personality traits may be more apparent than in every day life.

Some patients who are in hospital have suffered accidents and injuries which have left them mutilated and unpleasant to look at. Some patients have diseases which lay people look upon as 'unclean'. In these situations the patient may feel it necessary to withdraw from contact with others because he fears he is causing them discomfort or he is acutely aware of his own feelings of inadequacy.

When a nurse approaches a patient she expects him to react to her. It is normal for a person to respond in some way to one's advances.

When the patient does not react the nurse is apt to feel uncomfortable, to be anxious. The anxiety which is generated in her makes her withdraw from contact with the patient. A situation of mutual avoidance then exists and this perpetuates the patient's withdrawal. Because a nurse looking after a withdrawn patient feels unnecessary, she tends to be discouraged and feel helpless and her feelings are easily communicated to her patient.

It is, of course, easy just to 'solve' the problem by ignoring the patient – he is never any real trouble and does not complain of your neglect. Yet to do these things does nothing to meet the patient's needs. Positive action needs to be taken and could include:

1　Staying with the patient without necessarily speaking
2　Making contact whenever an opportunity presents itself during daily contact whilst carrying out routine tasks
3　Continuing a relationship once it has been established by 'coming back' to the patient especially when he expects you
4　It may be possible to 'mother' the patient whilst caring for his biological needs – this may help him feel more comfortable and hence more likely to respond to the nurse's attentions.

Physical contact with patients who are unpleasant to look at or who have such disorders as skin eruptions is usually an effective way of raising the patient's self esteem. This is by activities such as placing a hand on the patient's shoulder or perhaps holding his hand when helping him out of bed. Physical nearness between individuals is usually a way of communicating feelings without any words being spoken. It is also a component of what psychologists call intimacy. A patient responds to a gently, kind touch just as he responds to a feeling state which communicates fear.

Some other points to remember:

1 Seek alternative ways of approaching the problem
2 See each encounter with the patient as a challenge to the nurse's inter-personal skills
3 Be patient and sincere and expect variations in the patient's responses
4 Be aware of the fact that there is no substitute for persistence.

ANXIETY

Anxiety is perhaps the most frequently encountered psychological symptom in hospital and in most situations it is both reasonable and normal. Sometimes, however, a patient's anxiety is of such a magnitude that it is detrimental to his biological well being. It almost always indicates that some basic need is not being met.

Anxiety is also an important part of many other types of behaviour, eg:

1 Aggression
2 Withdrawal
3 Anorexia
4 Suicidal Pre-occupations
5 Attention Seeking
6 Immodesty

An acute bout of anxiety is probably the most extreme form of disturbed behaviour. For a normal person it is difficult to imagine what it is like — think of the dread, anguish or even terror that the patient experiences. When a patient is profoundly anxious he is almost always unaware of what is happening to him or indeed what effect his behaviour is having upon others.

His anxiety may cause him to be confused, he may shout or begin to act as though he were trying to escape from some physical danger.

When a patient's tension is very great it affects the reactions of the nursing staff. We are moved by the patient's anguish, by his suffering and his pain. This situation creates tension amongst the nursing staff. Another vicious circle has therefore been created.

Anxious and tense patients create tension in nursing staff. The reactions and ability of the staff to fulfil the patient's needs are impaired. The patient becomes more anxious.

How the disturbances arise is sometimes a matter of conjecture. We may postulate, however, that it is the result of uncontrollable internal forces and external or environmental influences.

In many instances there is good reason to be anxious. If one believes oneself to be dying or gravely ill, it is natural to worry about it. Real anxiety is more than just a natural reaction. There has normally been a gradual accumulation of anxiety. This anxiety is vague and difficult to specify and grows until it seems to the patient it will reach bursting point. The patient is usually unaware of the cause of his anxiety and may feel that he is unable to define it and, therefore, to talk about it.

In the patient's environment there are two main factors which affect him:

1 The patient's
2 The staff

When anyone is in the presence of anxiety he himself becomes anxious. In this situation anxiety between the patients is both created and maintained. If the nursing staff are anxious, upset, in conflict with each other, or are discouraged or uncertain about what their task is, these feelings are very quickly communicated to the patient. Because the patients are in continuous contact with the nursing staff, they are easily affected by the manifestations of serious disturbances and insecurity amongst the staff. The nurses therefore need to be aware of their reactions and how these affect the patient.

The nurse should therefore:

1 Be aware of the nurse's vulnerability to the patient's feelings of anxiety and take steps to cope with it
2 If a patient's anxiety or disturbed agitated behaviour is directed specifically towards the nurse, she may react by being angry, annoyed, or impatient. Recognizing these feelings will help her to deal with the patient

3 Often the nurse's attempts to protect herself from the patient's anxiety are subtle and difficult to be aware of. The nurse might, as a result, allow her focus to be severely restricted. It is necessary for her to recognize that she may be deliberately ignoring the patient's anxiety because she is unconsciously 'blocking it out'

4 Be aware of the patient's extreme anxiety. That is the only way possible to begin to alleviate it.

DEALING WITH THE SITUATION

Dealing with the anxiety of a patient is a difficult and challenging test. It is dependent upon the nurse's general understanding of the sources and nature of the disturbance.

It also depends upon the nurse's own reactions to the disturbance and on her experience and knowledge in handling the patients who are upset.

The most important point is to remember that anticipation of events may prevent a mild episode from becoming more serious. The nurse must know her patients and their usual ways of reacting and she should recognize the signs during the 'incubation period'. The signs may be revealed in:

1 The patient's face, ie his wrinkled brow; his anxious, drawn expression
2 In the way he moves about
3 The kind of gestures the patient makes
4 His speech is usually short and with a high pitch
5 Individual movements of the limbs, appear jerky and rapid
6 Occasionally the patient wrings his hands and paces the floor

If the nurse is alert to the signs she should be able to alleviate the anxiety in the initial stages with less effort than is required later. To be reassuring, she has to be able to withstand the patient's rejection and threats. She has to remember that he cannot control his behaviour and that telling the patient to 'pull himself together' is of no benefit.

Telling the patient simply to 'stop' is useful, however, because it implies to the patient that he is capable of doing so, that the nurse thinks he can achieve that much.

It might be necessary to define the situation for him, ie tell him where he is and who the nurse is, using language that is appropriate.

Other points to remember are:

1 The nurse must be willing to do something definite — to 'put herself out' for the patient
2 She should withstand her own anxieties
3 She should remember that the patient has other positive aspects without his anxiety — these should be utilized
4 'Persistence' is the key word
5 Efforts must be made over an extended period.

SADNESS

Sadness like anxiety is a normal reaction to certain situations. It would, for example, be abnormal not to be sad after a bereavement. Sadness, however, can be so severe as to impair the patient's ability to get well or even to carry out the daily business of living.

Sadness is an infectious disorder because we are all saddened, depressed and so on in the presence of someone who is sad.

Like the withdrawn patient, the sad patient is quiet and uncommunicative. He has characteristic signs and symptoms which may be observed:

1 He looks unhappy; his mouth droops at the corners and his brow may be wrinkled
2 He does not speak except when spoken to and even then he usually answers in short monotones
3 He has an impaired appetite
4 He has (or usually has) some disturbance of sleep
5 He does not respond in the usual way to environmental stimuli
6 He is preoccupied with his own thoughts and feelings and seems to have no time for relationships
7 He may cry with minimal provocation
8 He may become anxious.

Hospitals are, of course, places where sadness is generated daily. It is observed, for example, in:

1 A patient who is very ill
2 A patient whose family are suffering as a result of his illness
3 Patients with chronic and painful disorders
4 Those who are deeply affected by the sufferings of their fellow men.

All of these are likely to become sad and depressed.

There are some disorders which produce depressive symptoms due to organic disorder and some mental illnesses for which there is no known cause for a patient's depression.

It is easy to overlook the unhappy patient and indeed it is a usual reaction to withdraw from them. Having recognized from the signs and symptoms that the patient is unhappy the nurse is likely to develop vague feelings of apprehension that something is wrong with her. In the presence of unhappy people, she is likely to feel morbid or sad herself without knowing why.

The important point to grasp is that the patient is seeking the nurse's help even if he does not ask for it. If the nurse avoids him his feelings that he is not being helped will be increased along with his unhappiness. On the other hand an over effusive, exaggerated attention will make him uncomfortable and resentful. The problem is to establish an approach somewhere in the centre and avoid both extremes.

Some nursing points are:

1 By her daily contact with the patient the nurse should attempt to generate an air of optimism and cheerfulness
2 It is useful to help the patient achieve his daily routine by firmly holding him to his task, without coersion, eg if the patient has no appetite then the nurse should not ask him whether he would like his dinner, but should say 'I will fetch your dinner now'. The decision to eat has been taken away from the patient

3 The environment should be stimulating and cheerful with well lit, well ventilated colourful decorations and so on

4 The nurse can subtly draw attention to pleasant things and avoid his preoccupation with his problems

5 Obvious problems which can be solved by explanation or other means should be so dealt with

6 The nurse should realize that it is sometimes inappropriate for her to be cheerful and happy. In some situations it is necessary to gently comfort the patient and not introduce inappropriate cheerfulness.

SUICIDE

When patients are profoundly unhappy so much that living seems too much of a burden, they may feel it better if they died. A number of mental illnesses, of course, are characterized by suicidal preoccupation, but in a general hospital, episodes of attempted suicide are not unknown.

We take for granted that everyone wants to live as long as possible and that he will make some effort to do so. When the situation arises that is contrary to this idea the nurse feels threatened and insecure. When an 'incident' happens on a ward, the usual staff reaction is one of anxiety. Some indications that the patient is disturbed enough to attempt suicide are:

1 Direct or indirectly expressed thoughts about committing suicide

2 Preparations to do himself harm, eg storing medications

3 Behaviour which is unusual for the patient when he appears to be unhappy.

It is extremely difficult to tell by preliminary signs whether suicide is a real risk. To avoid a tragic mistake it is best to assume the worst and act accordingly.

By expressing suicidal feelings or indicating less directly that it may be possible, the patient is trying to communicate and may be telling us:

1 That his relationships with others are meaningless
2 That he is living without purpose or hope
3 That he sees no solution to his problems
4 That the pain and misery which he feels is too much for him to bear
5 That his 'need' is urgent and serious
6 That he wants someone to do something for him.

The nurse's task is to respond to his plea for help. If she does not do so the patient becomes more and more desperate. The nurse must make the patient feel that life is both necessary and desirable, to communicate to him that someone wants him to live and get well.

Each indication that suicide has entered the patient's thinking must be taken seriously and the patient has to be given immediate attention with sympathy and serious concern. The patient may appear to resent any attempt to curtail his freedom of movement and the continued observation by the nursing staff. In reality he will be thankful that his behaviour is going to be controlled. The law requires that the nurse takes reasonable precautions to prevent the ultimate act, but does not expect miracles. There is no truth whatever in the idea that if a patient is determined enough he will 'manage it'. The key is prevention since there is no cure should the patient achieve his intentions.

The situation should be evaluated in terms of how profoundly the patient feels. This is not too difficult if the nurse knows and has adequate relationships with her patient. She has to strike a balance between restriction and control. Some measures which should be undertaken are as follows:

1 The patient should be under constant observation day and night by nurses competent to cope with the situation
2 Possibility should be reduced if it cannot be eliminated. There are numerous environmental points to be kept in mind such as keeping rooms off the main ward out of bounds, supervising medication very closely, watching for materials and situations which present opportunity

3 Attention should be paid to the nurse/patient relationship and questions should be asked of it such as:

   (a)   Why does the patient feel unable to communicate his feelings to the nurse?

   (b)   Are the nursing staff allowing the patient to live through subjectively disturbing situations without adequate support from them?

   (c)   Does the nurse's behaviour and responses to the patient indicate a sincere desire to help?

   (d)   What positive measures can the nursing staff undertake to help the situation?

4 The key to the situation is:

> 'Attention is prevention'.

LOSS OF APPETITE (ANOREXIA)

It is a primary responsibility of a nurse to ensure that the patient takes an adequate diet to maintain and to improve his physical health. In many medical and surgical conditions the patient's appetite, due to physical symptoms, is the first casualty. This type of problem is, of course, a physiological one and the situation resolves itself when the patient recovers his health.

As a result of early infantile experiences, eating is associated with psychological satisfaction and security. Eating activities are therefore often an indication of anxiety and alterations in psychological well being. In some cases this alteration is associated with over-eating. In others it is responsible for the patient losing his appetite and refusing food.

Why does a patient have anorexia?

In part anyway, eating difficulties may be associated with the early experiences of an individual and it may be the patient's way of reacting to anxiety provoking situations. By and large, this situation is likely to be pathological and may be a recommendation for 'psychiatric treatment'.

In most cases, however, even though the patient has this way of reacting to situations, it may be perpetuated by the kind of interpersonal relationships which he is experiencing at a given period in time.

1 It may be directly a result of his interactions with the nurses
2 There may be dissatisfaction in eating or unpleasantness associated with food (he may have been 'conditioned' by his physical symptoms in early days of his illness)
3 He may eat reluctantly or with indecision or not at all

The ways in which the relationship he is having with his nurses may interfere with his eating are:

1 He may not like the attitude or manner of presentation of a particular nurse
2 The environment, ie the social setting in which he is eating may be unpleasant
3 He may feel that the nurses favour other patients more than him so that he is always served last or gets a less attractive meal
4 He may be too anxious, angry, irritated or sad because some psychological need has not been met
5 The meal-times may seem a burden to the nurses who 'rush it through' without thought.

Needless to say, a patient who does not take in adequate nutrition ultimately becomes dependent upon others for staying alive. The nurse's task is to help him assume responsibility for keeping himself adequately fed. The task is made more difficult if the nurse resents the extra burden of a busy mealtime and this may perpetuate the situation.

To break the stalemate, the nurse must develop a new orientation to the situation and convince the patient that she really cares about him.

It is necessary to talk to the patient about the situation in order to develop a consistent approach —

Inconsistency
Variation
Contradiction

all help to contribute to the patient's interpersonal problem.

Meal times should be conducted in an atmosphere of pleasant calm without hurry. If a patient indicates his reluctance to eat, perhaps by eating slowly, he should be given plenty of time and attention. The nurse should avoid getting irritated since this only perpetuates the difficulty. She should communicate the fact that she is willing to make an effort to help him make an effort. That she really cares whether he is eating or not. At some point the responsibility for eating will be transferred directly back to the patient — at this point the nurse should be ready to allow him the responsibility. She should make him feel that she knows he can manage it.

Other points to remember:

1 Eating is a biological necessity and adequate diet is a criteria of health
2 The difficulty may have arisen because some other need was not fulfilled
3 The manner of serving the meal and the situation under which it is served is important
4 The relationship between the server and the served affects the situation
5 The task is to identify and to eliminate the problem that caused the situation but other measures may help, eg
     Appealing to likes and dislikes
     Small portions
     Attractive presentation
6 Make use of fluctuations in the patient's problem. When he does want to eat, try to give him extra calories.

THE SLEEPLESS PATIENT

It is very difficult to obtain any rest during the day in hospital due to the constant coming and going in and about the ward. Yet, despite this fact, many patients in hospital are given sedatives and hypnotics to aid their night time sleep. Many of these, of course, are very necessary due to factors such as pain, discomfort and the symptoms of the patient's illness. A substantial number might well be given to patients who could well sleep without them if their needs were being met.

During sleep the body rejuvenates itself, we exist on low power so to speak. The excursions and exercises of the day which have used up reserves of energy are replaced by relaxation and rest. Sleep also serves another function in that during sleep it is postulated that the unconscious portion of the mind is able to 'act out' and relieve the tensions of the day during dreaming. We should awake from sleep therefore, rested and relaxed. Artificial sleep is known to inhibit this dream process and consequently patients taking sedatives and the like do not necessarily experience the relief of tension of the normal sleeper. The day is thus faced with a handicap of the previous day's tensions yet to be resolved. The situation produces a well-recognized vicious circle.

All this discussion leads us to a simply stated fact. This is that one of the central tasks in nursing is to ensure useful and normal sleep in the patients in order to help them recover their health more quickly. Promoting sleep is a nursing skill which is complementary to the central task of a nurse.

Patients who cannot sleep are a common phenomena to all nurses who have worked in the wards at night time. There are lots of reasons why a patient may have difficulty. Generally one advises the nurse to consider the environment, the physical state of the patient and his psychological well-being. In this text we are mainly concerned with the latter of these.

Some psychiatric illnesses for example, depressive illness produces the symptoms of insomnia. Some organic conditions produce a reversal of sleep-pattern so that the patient sleeps during the day and remains awake and active during the night. These are symptoms of specific disorder and little of what is said in this text may be of relevance to their situations. The majority of patients who cannot sleep cannot do so because of their anxieties. Hospitals are anxiety provoking places at the best of times. At night when other patients are asleep and the ward is dimly lit, the patient feels a greater sense of isolation. The control which he has managed to maintain during the day loses its grip on him because he is relatively unobserved. He does not have the support of the other patients or the ward routines to direct his attention away from his problems. The sensitivities are heightened because he is probably afraid and his basic needs of security, affection and so on are, therefore, greater.

It seems a paradox that night time is often a time when the number of staff on a ward is reduced to a minimum because a patient is likely to need the kind of support that a busy nurse is likely to overlook.

Most patients are more likely to talk freely at night to members of the nursing staff perhaps feeling the bond which is created between those awake when the lights are dim and most people sleeping.

In creating sleep, the nurse needs to consider and examine the needs of the patient at that moment in time. This is related to individuals and what is appropriate for one is not necessarily so for another. The nurse should, therefore, consider the following points.

Most people who are fearful are in need of the security afforded by another person. This implies that being near to a patient may in itself be enough to reassure them that the nurse is available if required. A regular visit to each patient and particular visits to sleepless patients is probably helpful.

If a patient wants to express his problems, he should be allowed to do so, just expressing them whilst receiving subjective support from the nurse, will help to relieve the tensions which they create.

Physical nearness is a component of intimacy and the security which that creates. A firm hand is reassuring and comforting to the patient.

If conversation takes place the nurse should avoid topics which are stimulating in themselves. The voice can be used as a sedative if the appropriate tones and suggestions are used.

Obvious worries which cannot be corrected or acted upon during the night, might be seen to the next day with a word of reassurance that some action will be taken, eg worry about the patient's family. If the nurse undertakes such a promise to the patient it is unthinkable that she should not see it through.

If there are factors in the environment which disturb the patient, they should be corrected.

5
Children

The human infant is usually born somewhere around 280 days after the date of the mother's last menstrual period. At birth an average infant weighs about 3 kilos and is approximately 56 cms long.

Birth is not, however, the beginning of the infant since a foetal heartbeat has been detected as early as four weeks of intra-uterine life. The pregnant mother feels her baby moving somewhere around 16 to 20 weeks. The four weeks which follow birth are known as the neonatal period and the baby as the neonate.

Birth itself used to be thought to be a traumatic experience and many psychologists have described situations which they have attributed to this trauma.

In physiological terms the process of being born is a profoundly exhausting experience and, as a consequence, much of the neonatal period is spent in sleeping whenever the baby is not feeding or crying. A certain amount of development, however, does take place. In the first week or so the baby is stabilizing his respiratory and heart ratio and soon after is beginning to be sensitive to certain varieties of stimulation. He is able to hear and is sensitive to visual experiences although we could not say he was able to 'see' in terms of adult sight.

By the end of the neonatal period the infant begins to experiment with various sensations by a process of trial and error and he will suck any pleasant object or substance which he finds. Some psychologists have suggested that these early 'experiments' which the child undertakes are the beginning of learning and 'thinking'. Others attribute them merely to inborn tendencies which we know as instincts.

The baby's first concern, however, is not with experimentations with visual or other experiences, but with the every day business of living. Accordingly his primary reason at that moment anyway for living is to fulfil his biological needs. When his biological needs are not met he expresses his concern by crying. Babies do not cry without reason and, although some crying which is not accompanied by tears is considered to be 'shouting', all forms of crying indicate that some need is not being met.

Basic needs which need to be met include:

1 Food

The infant requires food each time that he is hungry. He has no concept of time or of feeding schedules and will not consider it inappropriate to cry between feeds.

2 Warmth and Comfort

The young babies' heat regulating mechanism is not an efficient piece of apparatus and fluctuations in heat can be quite disturbing for the baby. Evacuations from the bladder and bowel are not under the control of the will and the baby is incontinent. When evacuations take place they cause the child discomfort.

3 Loving

The infant's development has been shown to be greatly influenced by his experiences in early childhood. Although a very young infant has not real concept of who his mother is, he requires to experience 'loving behaviour' from his mother or mother substitute. Feeding the infant affords a good opportunity for him to be close to his mother — in actual physical contact with her. Cuddling and picking the child up at other times, contrary to popular legend, does no harm and is beneficial for the infant who develops feelings of security and warmth and love.

Motor Development

The bulk of the development of the human infant takes place in the first three years of life.

Motor development assumes a much greater importance to parents than it justly deserves and late achievement in an infant is looked upon as some sort of intellectual deficit. In reality it is probably not possible to define exactly the expected ages of achievement for an infant but only to say what an 'average' child may achieve at an approximate age.

Early and late achievement of milestones is therefore probably not significant as far as later progress is concerned.

Two factors are concerned in the development of motor skills. These are:

1 Parental guidance and encouragement
2 The development of neuro-muscular mechanism to 'control' the act.

It is, therefore, impossible for an infant to stand, walk etc before a certain age.

It is a well recognized fact that parents who encourage the child to walk etc are likely to positively help the child. In cultures which swaddle their children, the children tend to walk and so on much later.

The following table serves to illustrate the approximate ages of development:

Neonate:	Lies with limbs flexed
	Muscles generally flaccid
	Has no head control
	Exhibits spontaneous movements, such as twitching and arching of the back
0:3	Has head control but still moves in unspecified manner
0:4	May attempt to turn over when lying prone and will 'smile'
0:8	Sits up in 'baby position' ie leaning on abdomen rather than sitting erect with back control. Some children crawl at this age

1:0	Stands. Can oppose fingers and thumb. Can pile up 2 bricks
1:2 - 1:8	Average child walks
	Girls usually walk before boys. Overweight children walk later and children who crawl well may lack incentive to stand and walk
2:0	Runs. Has developed high degree of manipulative skills and can pile up 6 building bricks.

SOCIAL DEVELOPMENT

The new born infant's brain and nervous system are not fully developed at birth and the sense organs are not fully receptive to stimuli except those of a profound nature. Hence a mother's joy at 'recognition' by the infant when he smiles at her is really somewhat optimistic since the child will react to the shape of a white place held in front of him in a similar manner.

Up to about seven months an infant is in a stage of development which is known as 'adualism'. This is a state first described by Piaget in which the infant has no self-awareness. It is unable to separate itself from its environment having no consciousness of objects about it. The state is resolved by the infant's exploration of its body and the immediate environment. It is not merely a developmental phase of little significance but is important because it suggests that having no concept of self it logically follows that the infant has no concept of others, including his mother.

Separation of the mother and child is therefore of little significance providing that the infant's essential needs are met adequately by a mother substitute or substitutes.

Somewhere about 6 to 10 months, usually about seven months, the adualism is resolved and the child is able to perceive others as permanent and independent.

Following this period of time in the infant's life there is a fundamental change in his social development. The infant becomes attached to the permanent figures in his environment and mother, being the primary person (due to her socio-biological role) is the person

person with whom the child's first relationship is formed.

The change from lack of discriminative to definite attachments is not sudden and probably begins to show itself when the infant expresses his desire for contact when he is left alone, by crying. Initially, the need for comfort and stimulation might be met by any one person, but the mother soon becomes most important.

During this stage of development the infant needs a lot of physical nearness to nurture his development and it might be noted how frequently mothers hug and cuddle their babies between the ages of about 8 months and one year. As the child becomes mobile the activity tends to decrease and even later at about two years much of the initiative for physical contact comes from the infant and a two year old can be observed exhibiting a lot of 'cuddling' and 'loving' behaviour.

Many factors are believed to influence the child's personality development in the early years and amongst them, separation from mother is very important. This is discussed under 'going to hospital' later.

Some authorities comment upon the need for mother to stimulate the child and, at the same time, to allow a developing independence culminating in going to school.

The infant behaviour generally shows many different phases and these might be summarised as follows:

0:7 months	Indiscriminate, unattached behaviour and total dependence for biological needs
7 months to 2 years	Profound development of relationship with permanent figures in the child's environment but especially with mother. Remains dependent for most needs
2 years, probably earlier, to 3/4 years	'Prima-Donna' stage when the infant begins to manipulate situations — an indication of the developing of less dependence. Some problems such as temper tantrums. Remains mainly attached to mother however. Friends, real or imaginary, are important

| 3/4 years | 'Debutante'. During this stage the child enjoys increasing her range of acquaintances and enjoys social gatherings and personal friends. Stage probably continues up to school age or a little later. |

When the infant begins schooling the changes include new attachments to adult figures such as teachers and to friends of his own age.

Group behaviour and the need for co-operation develop social behaviour.

This very brief account of the child's development is not intended to be in any way comprehensive and text books of development should be consulted for detailed accounts.

SOME AREAS OF SPECIAL INTEREST IN CHILD DEVELOPMENT RELEVANT TO NURSING

Play

Play activities are those activities which may be undertaken for their own sake and which give pleasure and satisfaction, whilst providing a break from the more taxing aspects of life. Play is a less serious but natural part of growing up and it is a necessary preparation for the mature development of personality.

Theories abound about the significance of play in a psychological sense. For practical purposes it suffices the nurse to understand that it is an essential feature of childhood and opportunities for play should be provided for children in all situations.

Uses of Play

Play performs a number of useful functions with regard to —

1 Physical growth
2 Intellectual growth
3 Emotional growth
4 Social growth.

Physically through play, a child is exercising and developing his body.

Various activities are helpful in the development of neuro-muscular co-ordination, eg hand and eye skilled movement, manipulative ability and so on. The child through play 'practises' movements and co-ordination and as a consequence lays down neural patterns within the nervous system. The long term results are seen when transfer of co-ordination or manipulative skills is effected to the business of living, eg a child playing at dressing her doll learns to dress herself as a result. She learns to manipulate buttons and fasteners and so on. During play activities the child is exposed to numerous sensory experiences and learns to discriminate colour, shape and texture.

Intellectual growth is achieved as the child enriches his range of experiences as he explores his environment. His play affords him opportunity to use his powers of imagination and creativity and provides practice in concentration, thinking and reasoning. Play enables him to cope with and make the necessary adjustments to life in a satisfactory way, thus contributing to an increasing self-confidence and independence.

Whilst participating in play activities a child is able to 'act out' his emotional problems, the activity which he is using, serving as the outlet for emotion. He is also able to develop emotional control since many play activities require of him that he behaves in a socially acceptable way, developing self discipline and respecting the rights of others. Play serves as a proving ground for language development and the child develops the child skills in comprehension and use of language. Through playing in groups the child acquires the ability to co-operate with others and to appreciate the benefits of team work. Group activities help to fulfil the child's emotional needs by providing group membership.

Observation of children's play activities has led some psychologists to suggest that certain activities are associated with inborn drives. During 'imitative' play the child may copy the behaviour of adults in such games as:

'Mothers and Fathers'
'Train Drivers'
'Doctors and Nurses'.

Certain games may have a similarity with the playing which young animals undertake as 'training' for hunting and so on. Later such games include 'hide and seek', soldiers, etc.

Apart from all this, play may well be described as a series of activities which are carried out for their own sake, ie leisure activities. These include things like

Hobbies
Discussions
Music
Team Games.

Planning Play Activities

Hospitals for sick children should provide adequate facilities in a range of suitable equipment, adequate space (play areas) and opportunities for private belongings and individual activities. There should be pleasant homely surroundings with relative freedom from common dangers although complete elimination, administratively necessary, is in danger of creating sterility.

If possible there should be regular 'play staff' whose function is to provide motivation and security of a more or less lasting nature. This is especially important when a child is in hospital for a long period but it does not eliminate the nurses from the play situation.

Attitudes to play should be positive and should be of an understanding nature about its uses and benefits.

Staff responsible for play should provide a warm co-operative atmosphere where the children are encouraged to explore and learn through play. A situation should be provided which enables experimentation in individual and group activities.

Suitable Play Activities

1 Dressing Up Games

Dressing up, especially in adult clothes gives a great deal of pleasure and offers valuable opportunity to exercise the imagination. Supplies of adult clothing, old shoes and so on should be freely available

2 Models

Miniature versions of actual objects (farm animals, cars, dolls and dolls' houses etc all have value by improving the child's knowledge of colour, shape, size and classification.

Providing the nurse plays and talks with the children regularly, models help by encouraging speed

3 Nature

Nature study, having natural things pointed out, collecting items of interest and having displays in the play area of the ward all increase the child's awareness of the environment, colour, shape, texture and growth.

4 Animals

Keeping animals as pets may not seem appropriate in a hospital ward, but they serve to help the child develop gentleness. They are educational and may provide an opportunity for the child to give affection to a living organism. Animals which could not of course be kept in situations where they would interfere with the medical situation, eg where they might cause infection.

Mentally Handicapped Children and Play

Play is extremely important for the mentally handicapped child. It enables the child to develop along normal lines. Mentally handicapped children have a reduced interest and inquisitiveness and in addition over-activity or social isolation may be a feature of their disorder. Certain physical handicaps such as spasticity or sensory defects pose numerous difficulties.

Some handicapped children have fixed ritualistic play habits. In hospitals for the mentally handicapped and mentally disturbed children, play is used both as a diagnostic and therapeutic tool.

For further information on the topic of play and the mentally retarded, readers are referred to the book 'Mental Deficiency' in the Modern Practical Nursing Series.

Crying

During the neonatal period, crying in babies is really a form of communication since the baby is attempting to 'tell' the person caring for him that he is hungry, uncomfortable or whatever. Observation of very young babies will help prove this hypothesis since they can be observed 'crying without tears'.

Soon after the neonatal period the baby begins to exhibit various types of crying as a more sophisticated way of communicating even though the child does not consciously do so. These include:

'Wetting Cry'

This is the crying which during the neonatal period has indicated that the baby has soiled and requires changing for his comfort. At about six weeks the baby is able to accept the fact of 'wetness' and the cry begins to diminish in frequency.

'Sleep Cry'

In the early days, most babies cry prior to going to sleep ie when they are fatigued. This type of crying diminishes progressively over a long period until it finally disappears around about the age of 3.0.

'Hunger Cry'

The baby cries perhaps most frequently because it is hungry. As the child begins to be able to delay satisfactions, the hunger cry diminishes and except on special occasions it usually disappears at about 2.0.

Most mothers who have had wide experience in child rearing, claim to be able to distinguish one cry from another so that she is able to anticipate the infant's need on hearing the cry.

From her point of view, the nurse should realize that babies and children do not cry without reason.

If crying is evident then it indicates that some essential need is not being met or that the infant is attempting to communicate some difficulty.

Crying for long periods is physically exhausting and should never be allowed to continue in the mistaken belief that giving the required attention will 'spoil' the child.

When no obvious physical need is evident, it can be assumed that the need is for love and physical nearness and the child should be picked up and nursed. There are no documented instances where babies and children have suffered damage because they have not been allowed to cry for long periods.

Regression in Toilet Habits

Most children in hospital 'go back' in their toilet habits and previously continent children may soil or wet themselves whilst in hospital.

This is a normal phenomena and is probably directly related to the age of the child since younger children regress more frequently. Sometimes, of course, the symptom is one of emotional disturbance. In all cases sympathy and understanding are the key words and disciplinary measures should not be attempted in the mistaken belief that the child 'should know better'.

Eating

Children are often anorexic or eat voraciously for emotional reasons. Usually, however, in illness (with specific therapeutic exceptions) eating is best left to the child's own desires of the moment. Evidence suggests that a child left to his own devices will eat a reasonably balanced diet even though at times he appears not to.

A child, despite the adult beliefs to the contrary, usually knows best what he can and cannot take at a particular time. There should be no panic about nutritive requirements since many young children use the adult's anxieties as a means of manipulating the situation. Whenever it is possible, the nurse should attempt to appeal to the child's preferences. It is worth noting once again that eating is often directly related to emotional comfort and an anorexic child may well have essential emotional needs unmet.

Sleep

A child's sleep may be disturbed by nightmares and night terrors. Either or both of these phenomena, if they are common, may be an indication that the child is seriously disturbed and requires specialized help.

In hospital, some disturbance of the child's sleep is almost

71

inevitable since he does not expend the usual amount of energy during the day and the new and strange environment is disturbing enough in itself. Add to this the high degree of anxiety and physical discomfort which might be present and one can anticipate difficulty.

Going to sleep or being 'bedded down' for the night should be an enjoyable experience for children.

It begins with a running down of the day's activities when exciting the child or over stimulating him is to be avoided. There should be stories, cuddling and loving activity and whenever possible the child's usual comforter should accompany him to hospital. These might range from his favourite teddy to a familiar piece of old blanket.

For very young children, it is often best to tell the same story, one with a pleasant tale and ending, frequently for it brings with it a feeling of familiarity and security. Older children of course would soon become bored and demand a little more effort.

Telling stories to children is useful in as much as morality and guidance may be 'got over' using the characters spoken of — a process of identification being operative.

Whenever there appears to be disturbance of sleep the following might be considered:

1 The Environment

Are there noises, light, disliked neighbours and so on, keeping the child awake? Does he usually sleep in a cot or bed? Is he warm enough or too hot?

2 Psychological Factors

Is the child anxious or emotional due to being in hospital or are there fears which are disturbing him? Might his disturbance be the result of parental loss?

3 Physical Factors

Is the child in pain or just merely uncomfortable? Has he been told how to find the best sleeping position with regard to his condition? Is he hungry or have one of the thousands of minor ailments which disturb us all? An important factor in a child's case is whether he has been told about toilet arrangements.

Going to Hospital

There are, as previously mentioned, periods in the child's life when being separated from his parents and mother in particular, is more important than at other times. The critical period is probably somewhere between seven months and up to about three years.

At this age the mother is, in the child's comprehension, the most important protector and provider for needs. During this phase of his development a child never strays far from his mother and even when he plays with friends or alone outside he makes frequent journeys back to the house to reassure himself that mother is still available should he need her.

Should any incident occur to hurt or disturb him he returns immediately to his mother for the solace and comfort he knows will be available.

At this age he exhibits much spontaneous loving behaviour and will frequently climb on to his mother's knees and kiss and cuddle her. All this, of course, is a natural phase in his developing social relationships and uninterrupted periods of mothering lay the basis for future relationships and, indeed, mental health. Going to hospital or separation from his mother for any other reason is a major upheaval for him and even short periods which have been inadequately prepared for, have lasting traumatic effects.

To the child, yet unable to comprehend the significance of separation, the situation is comparable to bereavement due to the death of his mother. Being unable to understand, the child exhibits signs and symptoms not dissimilar to the classical features of mourning seen in a bereaved adult. These signs and symptoms occur in three distinct phases, viz:

1 Protest

Protest is the initial phase and lasts for hours, days and in some cases even weeks. The child is desolate at the loss of his mother. He is stricken with grief and is frightened and confused by the unfamiliar sights and sound going on around him. He makes ineffective attempts to recapture his mother and cries loudly and is extremely excitable. Any sign that Mum may be returning immediately captures his attention so that he will watch a door opening or turn quickly at the sound of footsteps and, in all cases, his burden of despair is heightened when the expected appearance does not materialize.

He needs comfort at this time, but may reject adult attempts to help him.

2 Despair

The child's feelings of protest gradually give way to a state of despair. He has feelings of increasing hopelessness for he has abandoned the idea of his mother's return. He becomes withdrawn and apathetic and his quietness leads the insensitive to think that he is over his disturbance and has settled in. If mother visits the child during this period he is likely to protest loudly once again when she leaves. The usual staff reaction is to claim 'visits from mother upset the child'. In reality his disturbance which he has managed to 'control' has emerged once again.

3 Denial

The child may or may not proceed to a third phase, that of denial. The mechanism of denial is used to deny that mother is necessary. The child becomes centred on material things which to him are reliable comforts. His behaviour is ego-centric and he often reacts to situations with aggression. If his mother reappears at this time he may not respond and may well reject her altogether.

Prolonged periods of deprivation result in lasting effects upon the infant's personality. The 'rehabilitation' necessary even after relatively short periods may take many months.

The effects of deprivation of mothering are not necessarily proportional to the length of deprivation and numerous factors contribute to and aggravate the situation. These might include:

1 The preparation for the child's hospitalization or temporary loss of mother
2 The hospital admission procedure and nursing methods
3 The staff of the hospital
4 The parents of the child

Preparation for Hospitalization

There are many conflicting ideas as to how a child might be prepared for a period of hospitalization. In general it is necessary to say that in a great number of cases no preparation is undertaken and the process is more traumatic as a result. If a child's scheduled to be hospitalized then his parents and the hospital should co-operate to make the event as easy as possible.

Probably the most useful way of preparing the child is to make a preliminary visit to hospital if possible to the ward in which he will stay. Prior to the visit, mother should begin to introduce 'hospital' into topics of conversation and stories of hospital are useful to enable the child to 'identify' with the characters of the story.

Games might be played related in some way to the procedures which are going to be undertaken in this respect. The child can play at 'hospitals' with his teddy or whatever.

On arrival at the hospital for his visit, the child should be welcomed and shown around with mum by a nurse who is likely to look after him when he is admitted. He should be shown his bed or cot and other children who seem to be enjoying themselves. There is not, of course, any ideal which will eliminate altogether the trauma of admission. The aim should be to reduce it to a minimum.

The Hospital Admission Procedure and Nursing Methods

All the phases of disturbance which are exhibited by the child during separation are accentuated by the child's handling during admission and the type of nursing system which is in force.

The primary task is to ensure that all nursing staff are aware of the nature of the child's experience and the effect it may have on him. The second most important task is to do the minimum to the child during the admission procedure.

It should, for example, be possible to allow the child's mother to bathe him at home prior to coming to the hospital or, if it is absolutely necessary, to allow the mother to bathe him at the hospital. Ideally, there should be unrestricted visiting for parents so that they may take part in the child's care and avoid the deprivation effects mentioned. Alternatively, and even better, mother should be allowed to reside with the child in the hospital. Efforts should be made to have one nurse to take the child through the procedure and this nurse should be competent to perform the necessary tasks with skill and consideration. If the child's mother has to go away then the staff should constantly reassure the child of her return, but should never use statements which are untrue and promise things which do not materialize.

Mother is, of course, the best nurse of all since as it has been pointed out she requires no off-duty, can manage almost without sleep and is profoundly protective of her sick child. The child's mother is able to instinctively anticipate the child's needs and knows more thoroughly than the best nurse his mannerisms and responses.

Sadly, however, many circumstances prevent this ideal being accomplished and in these situations the system of nursing should attempt to replace the mother with a substitute to provide continuous and effective care. This is best accomplished by what is called 'family group nursing' where one nurse is given the responsibility for a group of children whose entire needs she sees to. Although no one disputes the efficacy of this system, often it is not used since expediency demands and, indeed, creates a system of task orientated care. If the family group method is used, junior nurses require a good deal more supervision from their seniors.

Alternative to this system there has been suggested 'mothering ladies' who are lay persons employed to provide the child's psychological needs during his hospitalization. These ladies usually care for one or two children, attempting to develop an emotionally satisfying relationship to replace the child's mother. In long stay hospitals, school teachers may fulfil this role with older children.

The Hospital Staff

All the processes of deprivation in the infant are accentuated and prolonged because most people in caring situations become dulled to the child's unhappiness by a process of time. They accept the degree of disturbance as the inevitable sequence of the child's admission. Some years ago when the writer's child was a patient in hospital, observation of the nursing and domestic staff in the paediatric ward indicated how the detachment from the child patients seemed to grow with seniority.

The persons who seemed most concerned about the child's disturbance were the most junior members of the hospital staff. Those least concerned were the most senior. It is not one might add necessarily the usual situation, but the fact that such a situation existed at all was very disturbing in itself.

Because sick children are a sad phenomena anyway and one is affected more deeply at the suffering of a helpless child, the staff of paediatric wards and so on tend to become blunted and to use the mechanism of denial to help themselves to survive emotionally in such a situation.

When an infant is 'despairing' it is, of course, easy to believe that he has 'settled in' and many staff interpret his quietness as a sign that he has got over his unhappiness.

Nurses in a paediatric ward need a high degree of sensitivity and a sincere wish to understand and help the child to be least harmed in a traumatic situation. Some positive measures which might help are:

1 The staff at the hospital should keep themselves aware of dangers at becoming 'blunted' in the caring situation

2 Senior staff members should attempt to develop awareness in the junior members

3 Hospital routine should include periods set aside each day in the paediatric ward for the nurses to pay special attention to the childrens' emotional needs

4 Procedures necessary but unpleasant, should be followed by periods of cuddling and physical contact with the children

5 Certain activities should be social occasions, eg meal times.

The Parents

It is not only the staff of the hospital who need education, for many parents are only too ready to give their children completely into the care of the hospital.

Parents should be given preliminary information perhaps in the form of a booklet explaining the situation to them. They should be encouraged to be involved in the day to day care of their child and should at least visit as frequently as possible.

It is often useful to the hospital staff if the child's mother could supply a brief guide to the child's likes and dislikes in terms of eating, sleeping and so on, and the child's communication characteristics.

For example, how does the infant usually ask to use the toilet etc. Although some authorities stress the importance of the mother in the situation, the father can equally be encouraged to fulfil the need should mother be unavailable.

Some Psychological Disturbances which take Place in Childhood

There are many disorders of childhood which are of a psychological nature. The bulk of these are probably concerned with educational backwardness and all of its many ramifications and forms of mental illness specific to or manifested in childhood. We are concerned with neither of these, but rather with unfortunate situations, habits and behaviour which normal infants may demonstrate at some time or other. The sort of habit and so on are those which a parent or teacher would make efforts to correct were they present in sons, daughters or children in their care.

Nurses are concerned with such problems because they need to be able to differentiate between what is so profound as to be pathological and that which is a minor indication of a need for greater understanding and attention.

The majority of the disorders which are mentioned are not caused by an endogenous disturbance in the child, but from faulty parental management and environmental factors. The solution therefore to the bulk of these problems is probably attention to both parent and child together. For more detailed accounts of these problems and their therapy the reader is referred to specialized text books. This account attempts to inform about misconceptions and guide the nurse in her daily interactions with her younger patients.

Aggressiveness

The development of control over our feelings is a gradual process and control of this nature is not seen in very young children. Episodes of aggressiveness and temper tantrums are seen frequently in children of this age and are manifested as bouts of screaming, kicking and uncontrolled rage.

In literature there are many examples and accounts of the real nature of the human organism and there are those who believe the human infant capable of the most destructive deeds were he physically able to accomplish them.

As time goes by, the bounds of acceptable behaviour are defined for the child and his growing maturity enables him to postpone gratification of instinctive needs and urges. He learns to control his anger at being denied them. Temper tantrums therefore are a normal developmental phase which are frequently seen around the age of two years (The 'Prima Donna' stage).

When they persist after this time or when they are of a violent and frequent nature, they may indicate that the child is not, or has not, learned to postpone gratification and the cause should be sought in the family atmosphere and the parental anxieties.

In general a child learns to control urges by having the bounds of his behaviour defined for him in the form of parental guidance. This is not possible when the guidance is not consistent. A general atmosphere of security (a basic psychological need) should be generated with firm discipline and not necessarily of a physical nature. During an actual tantrum the child will respond to help by physical nearness (cuddling) and calmness in reacting to them. A popular belief that the incident should be 'ignored' because it is 'attention seeking' is not correct.

Jealousy

Jealousy between children in the same family is a very common phenomena and the first born is usually jealous of the second born and so on. Jealousy is sometimes a cause of temper tantrums and seem to occur more frequently in girls. Once again the family atmosphere is the all important factor since jealousy amongst children is much more common when the parents create an atmosphere of competitiveness rather than co-operation between their children.

For obvious reasons the first born child who is displaced from her premier position in the family into second place by the new born baby, is often the one who experiences jealousy most profoundly. Jealousy may be exhibited in a variety of ways, all of which are an indication that the child needs for security and affection are not being met. The ways of expressing these needs include bedwetting, anxiety, temper tantrums and, most frequently, regression to an early level of development. This is, of course, a way the child sees of 'imitating' the new baby to attract his mother's attention since she apparently responds to her baby's similar behaviour. Regression may involve 'going back' in toilet habits, a desire to be fed (sometimes shown as food refusal) and efforts to be given physical comfort by seeking mother's attention by overt forms of behaviour. The child does not understand the process and management should never in any circumstances involve punishment for his baby-like behaviour.

A family which generates security for its children does so by providing co-operation not competition and by giving affection physically and otherwise to all its children alike.

When a new baby is expected, the older child should be told about the new arrival and should be involved in any necessary preparations.

When the baby comes along, he should be allowed to 'help' and his natural curiosity given range of freedom.

It is sometimes useful for mothers to set aside a time of day, perhaps before bedtime, when she can give the older child her undivided attention.

A complicating factor when the child is relatively young and mother goes into hospital for her second child is the added effects of maternal deprivation.

Lying

Even George Washington in his early days was subject to not always telling the absolute truth.

Young children may 'lie' for numerous reasons. Up to about four years fantasy and a vivid imagination is expressed in falsehoods. At this time, children also tell what is not true in order to fill in gaps in their understanding. In these cases the infant readily confesses his misdeed when confronted with it and admits, as it is usually expressed, that he was 'pretending'.

Later, lying is used by children as a means of escaping punishment or as a means of gaining attention.

Pathological lying is in fact quite uncommon in childhood but when it does occur it should be dealt with with understanding rather than punishment. The early days of a child's life should involve use of the idea that telling lies is not pleasant and honesty is a valuable asset.

Bed Wetting (Enuresis)

Control over bladder sphincter is usually achieved by about the third year of infancy. Although there are numerous reasons why control may not be acquired, enuresis is considered to be an indication of some psychological disturbance. Most frequently enuresis is a night time phenomena since remaining dry at night is achieved later than in the daytime in a normal infant. As with many of the common disturbances of childhood (enuresis is about 5%) the cause of enuresis is not really understood. Undoubtedly, there is an environmental influence which includes such factors as sibling jealousy, parental anxiety and deprivation of maternal affection.

Enuresis sometimes occurs after the child has achieved cortical control over mictuition and, in these cases, which usually occur between four and seven years the cause is usually stress in the home environment.

Like the causes, the treatment of enuretic children have always been a matter of opinion and include psychotherapy of some kind, parental guidance and numerous physical methods such as 'bladder drills', drugs and physical devices designed to wake the sleeping child.

Some years ago there appeared in the medical press an article on the treatment of enureses. The article reviewed the various methods at the physicians' disposal including a piece of physical apparatus which was placed in the child's bed. Whn the child 'wet' the bed an electric circuit was completed which rang a bell and wakened the child. In response to this article a well-known psychiatrist wrote a letter saying that such an apparatus might be constructed by the parents of the enuretic child.

The writer of the original article then replied saying that such a suggestion was ridiculous. The psychiatrist pointed out that he had missed the subtle implication − if the parents were interested, the child would not be wetting the bed in the first place.

Enuretic children are sometimes found in hospital for investigation and assessment. In such circumstances it is not unusual for his enuresis to disappear.

In the household it is probably best to 'ignore' the problem as much as possible without reacting too strongly when the child has a dry night or a wet one. When the child's behaviour is no longer necessary, it ceases to be exhibited.

Constipation and Encopresis

Constipation is sometimes manifest in a young child because of parental attitudes. A child who is incontinent of urine is bad enough, but one who is incontinent of faeces is in a very unfortunate position. Control of bowel movements assume ritual importance in early infantile experiences and over solicitous mothers are likely to cause the child to hold his stools longer than is necessary rather than to be incontinent. Such children usually suffer a chronic form of constipation. An infant may also hold on to his stools longer than necessary as a means of manipulating his parents (having realized their anxiety) and to seek attention. The solution to the problem would seem to be education of anxious parents and attention to the child's psychological needs to remove the necessity for attention seeking behaviour.

Encopresis is incontinence of faeces after the age of three years or thereabouts. It is more common in boys and has a greater incidence between five and ten years.

Encopresis may be due to chronic constipation occurring for the above reasons. However, it is usually due to the child's anxieties about asking to go to the toilet and so on until a crisis intervenes. This is encountered when the child is in a 'new' situation such as starting school. Encopresis is sometimes an indication of emotional upset and an unfortunate one since parents are likely to react to the situation in inappropriate ways.

Occasionally it is encountered in families where the child has simply not been toilet trained.

Treatment once again centres around examination of family life and the forces acting within it. Education of parents being a cardinal principle.

Eating

Eating is associated with emotional satisfaction from an early age and unconscious memories of being suckled by one's mother are present in most people. It is not surprising therefore that disturbances of the patterns of eating in a child sometimes indicate emotional disturbance. These can take the form of either failure to eat, ie anorexia (loss of appetite) or as a voracious appetite (over-eating).

Most parents are familiar with the fact that at certain ages children have less of an appetite than at others.

It is not unusual for babies who are being weaned from fluid to solid diets to 'go off' their food. This is also true as a developmental phase during the ages of 2 and 3 years. When the child is especially likely to use the situation to manipulate the parents. Children of this age usually go through a negative stage anyway. When children begin to play away from the household they are sometimes so pre-occupied that they forget to go for meals.

Perhaps more important factors in a child's loss of appetite is general feelings of anxiety and unhappiness which can ensure for a number of reasons. Parental influences in the form of nagging and anxieties about nutrition may also cause rather than cure the situation. Mealtimes in the family should be a social gathering with pleasantness in a situation where all the family meet together. Left to their own devices most children eat a reasonable diet — only when something is wrong do they fail to do so.

Other measures aimed at correcting the situation by appealing to the child include small meals with no snacks between meals, appealing to preferences and measures involving reinforcers.

Over-eating, although the opposite of anorexia, is usually associated with similar household situations.

Taking of foods acts upon all of us as a relief of tension and children who are in the need of emotional comfort may turn to food as an opportunity to achieve some dependable satisfactions. Over-eating is also associated with maternal deprivation as previously mentioned. Treatment is of the cause.

Anxious children should be given emotional satisfaction and affection and discordant family life should be attended to.

Unpleasant or Unacceptable Habits

There are numerous pieces of behaviour which might be listed under this heading, all of which are usually grouped together as 'gratification habits'. That is, the habit is indulged in for purposes of some satisfaction which it serves, but which is probably not socially acceptable in most circumstances. They include such habits as nail-biting, thumb sucking, teeth grinding, picking at the skin, and masturbation.

Most of these habits have at some time or other been the centre of much divided opinion. All attract more attention than necessary. To be considered as an indication of some emotional dissatisfaction they need to be persistent. In these circumstances they indicate the need for parental guidance and examination of the child's personal and family life.

6

Puberty and Adolescence

Puberty is a period of rapid physiological maturation during which there is maturation of reproductive function. There is redistribution of body tissues and a great increase in hormonal activity. The end result of these is the development of secondary sexual characteristics.

Occurring concurrently with and perhaps heralded by puberty is the developmental stage known as adolescence. This is a period of emotional and social changes which mark the transition from childhood to adult life.

Adolescence is not really a worldwide phenomena since in primitive societies the gap between childhood and adolescence is often no more than an initiation ceremony. In Western society, however, it is an elongated process which is filled with education and training which demand completion before 'success' can be anticipated in an adult-dominated society.

Because of these changes taking place in adolescence, the hospitalization of the adolescence creates numerous problems for the nurse caring for adolescent patients. If the hospitalization and treatment is to be affected with minimum disturbance, knowledge of these changes, their manifestations and how to deal with them is essential to the nurse. The situation is further complicated by the fact that many nurses are little beyond adolescence themselves.

The problems associated with the hospitalization of the adolescent derive from three main areas:

1 Physiological changes and their consequences
2 Emotional changes
3 Social changes.

Physiology

It is not necessary here to go into a long description of the physiology of puberty. It will suffice to say that the pubescent patient in the early stages anyway, is almost always clumsy, easily fatigued and unable to sit or stand for more than short periods without 'lounging'.

Further he is acutely aware of his inadequacies in these spheres and when his clumsiness manifests itself, if attention is drawn to it, it produces intense embarrassment.

Maturation of sexual characteristics makes the adolescent extremely shy and creates problems when examinations and procedures are carried out.

Emotional

Adolescence follows on a long period of sexual latency when the child is not preoccupied with sexual matters, but rather concerned with group activities and learning. Adolescence brings with it a change to hetiero-sexuality with the adolescent being very interested in the opposite sex. His successes or failures in his romantic contacts does much to influence his moods and attitudes on a day-to-day basis.

Also at this time there is a re-appearance of a developmental phase which has been described as the 'oedipus situation'. This simply is concerned with relationships with the parent of the same sex. This re-appearance of feelings of hostility towards the parent of the same sex is difficult for the adolescent to handle or to understand and leads to some confusion in self value. Because many persons in positions of authority are sometimes seen as parent figures, the difficulty which the adolescent would normally have with his parent is transferred to the parent figure. This is true of the adolescent's teachers and older staff encountered in hospital — eg Ward Sisters.

The average adolescent experiences conflict in regard to analysis of self values in preparation for adult life. These may influence him to rebel against or to resist the influences of adults around him, whose values he rejects.

These emotional changes compound to produce a moody, somewhat irritable, shy individual. Being aware of his inadequacies only too well, he may erect a facade of truculence and bad manners. His conflicts and feelings make him inarticulate, he becomes easily bored and concerned deeply with his success or failure.

Social

Because of the gap between adults and adolescents and the uniqueness of each new generation, there is often lack of understanding between the two groups. Being unable to act like a child (he looks like an adult) yet being disallowed to act as an adult (he is immature) the adolescent turns to his peers and adopts attitudes interests and even the dress of their 'group'. Being thus a homogenous group, adults are denied entry to the adolescent's real world. It follows logically, therefore, that the adult who finds herself nursing such a patient may well discover to her folly when she attempts to interact with him as an equal. Similarly, a negative approach which rejects the adolescent's opinions out of hand, talks at him rather than to him, and generally dismisses him as being of no opinion or status, is likely to be equally rejected by the adolescent. Interactions, therefore, must always be upon a positive or, at least, neutral basis.

Nursing the Adolescent

To draw attention to his inadequacies is probably the single most traumatic experience one could occasion upon the adolescent. The approach should be frank yet tactful, avoiding drawing attention to his clumsiness. Procedures should be carried out with a 'casual' air so as to minimize the embarrassment he must inevitably feel. There should be explanations prior to procedures and questions (often used to deny or confirm fears) should be answered honestly yet carefully above all avoiding ridicule when they appear to be unsophisticated and awkward.

Moodiness and truculence should be accepted with consistency without criticism or irritability. Active measures to prevent boredom such as occupational tasks, help about the ward and so on should be encouraged where appropriate. If the adolescent patient is bad mannered, by far the best influence and that most likely to change him is undoubtedly example.

When the nurse of more mature years interacts with the patient, she should accept from the outset that she is unable to interact as his peer, but is likely to be respected if she accepts this situation. Consistency is the keyword with adolescent patients just as with infants. There is some evidence to suggest that the adolescent finds points to respect in both authoritarian and permissive adults providing they are consistent. It is also suggested that many are thankful for conversation with an adult intelligent enough to be prepared to listen and accept their inarticulateness. The younger student nurse is at an advantage. In general she is likely to be accepted as a peer and can, therefore, readily develop relationships. The execution of nursing procedures can be undertaken in a friendly relaxed manner. On the other hand the adolescent patient may well feel more embarrassed when confronted with an 'equal' carrying out some personal procedure. Judging the situation and applying the appropriate approach usually comes with experience.

7
Maturity and Middle Age

What exactly constitutes maturity in an individual is a matter of some controversy. What can be said is that the definition undoubtedly differs from culture to culture, place to place and perhaps even person to person.

A mature individual is one who has developed a compromise between his own desires (perhaps his own instinctual desires) and the demands of society. He has learned to accept that all things are not readily available and that many 'satisfactions' have to be delayed or postponed indefinitely. The freedom of an individual is bounded by the dependence which he has upon his friends, neighbours and his home. He has to behave in a certain way to be acceptable as a member of the many parts of society. Mature adjustment enables self-reliance and the anger of a mature person is usually a result of threats to his family. His own self-esteem should be able to survive the imaginary 'slights' which characterize adolescent vexations. Mature individuals are able to give and exchange love and to form relationships which are meaningful and satisfying. He is able to make decisions confidently and carry disappointment with equanimity.

A mature individual coming into hospital should have no difficulty in adjusting to a new situation. Nevertheless his needs are not those of an adolescent or those of the confused geriatric patient. They are directly related to the psychological need created by his illness and hospitalization. The methods employed to deal with him are not markedly different from those of any other age group, but they might be accomplished in a different way.

A mature patient is very likely to have been influenced prior to coming to hospital by the public image of hospitals. This is because his range of experiences and, consequently, his exposure to media and other people, is greater than for example an adolescent patient. As a result, surprisingly enough, the mature patient may have even more anxieties about hospitals than 'less informed' patients. Because he is accustomed to it, he will expect information and will expect his questions to be answered in a straightforward manner. It must be disconcerting to abandon oneself to young nurses probably as old as one's children. The middle-aged or mature patient may initially, therefore, have difficulty in adjusting to the situation. (Many hospitals encourage regression for this reason. Younger nurses have minimal difficulties manipulating patients who have regressed).

Regression, however, does not solve the adjustment in a healthy way and may 'teach' the patient to use unhealthy mechanisms when subject to stress of any sort subsequently.

Most mature individuals have a high degree of self insight and, therefore, may adjust to irritations and restrictions of hospitalization quite easily. He appreciates, however, precise information so that his restrictions, although largely up to him to obey, are defined well in advance. Much of this information can be disseminated in the form of handouts. A mature individual is also able to profit from previous experiences and initial problems encountered in hospital may soon be dispelled by his use of judgement.

If problems do exist in terms of anxieties or the sometimes inevitable frustration of desires, an opportunity for sublimation should be provided to avoid conflicts.

Doctors and nurses have a great deal of power. Much more than the average one of them realizes. It is fairly easy to create situations and manipulate people of younger ages or, indeed, aged patients. Most difficult to manipulate are the middle-aged patients since they are likely to see the situation and react against it.

The process, therefore, is once again involving the patient in decision making, allowing him to directly express criticism and anxiety and being sensitive to his needs. The nurse's interactions should not be coloured by personal prejudices since a mature individual is not only more sensitive to these, but has himself developed his own particular 'stands' and may be quite rigid. Meeting his psychological needs expressed in Chapter 4 is the key to the situation.

8

Old Age

Aged patients for obvious reasons form a large part of the population of hospitals. The deterioration which comes with age is related both to physiological changes and psychological ones. This is so, not only because of the psychological changes associated with physical decline, but with other factors less well defined.

Probably 25% of all people are unfit by the time they retire from work. It is, however, a mistake to believe that age brings with it a decline in the ability to do heavy work. Indeed it is probably a fact that older men can accomplish quite heavy work, even well beyond the age of retirement. Old people, however, are generally slower to complete tasks, but remain conscientious for a long period of time. It has been said that working beyond the age of retirement keeps an aged person healthy since morbidity can be related to the age of retirement.

As with most other situations, the care of the older patient is directly related to meeting their essential needs.

It is proposed to outline some of the problems associated with ageing, the needs which these problems create and some measures which a nurse might undertake to make the patient's life more pleasant.

Memory

Difficulty in remembering comes to most of us quite early in life and the average middle-aged person requires a diary to keep him up to scratch. The degree of memory change varies greatly from individual to individual and some people are old at fifty years whilst others are alert and attentive even at 70 or 80 years.

Another factor which complicates the situation, and leads to an erroneous belief that the patient does not remember well, is their inability to adapt well to change. This is sometimes mistaken for lack of comprehension but is due to rigidity of ideas and methods. Most of us by the time we are thirty have made a stand one way or another on issues such as politics and so on. We increasingly become more dogmatic and routined in the business of living as time goes on. Add to this even a minor degree of memory deterioration and we need to cling even more to routines.

When there is definite evidence that memory disturbance is a feature of old age, the following may be of use:

1 A fixed routine should be adhered to to help the patient to be able to anticipate the days' events well ahead and possibly prepare for them
2 Detailed instructions cannot be given to aged people with memory disturbance and when it is necessary instructions should be written down and the aged patient reminded of them
3 Involvement in routines and procedures help the patient to overcome feelings of inadequacy regarding his deficit.

Sensory Deficit

Old age in our society tends to bring with it much social isolation. Young and middle-aged people often cannot be bothered to spend time with old people. If the aged person suffers a sensory deficit such as loss of hearing or failing vision, his isolation is greatly increased. He is likely to lose track of current events and be unable to communicate his needs adequately.

Specific action might be taken to minimize the difficulty with the provision of hearing aids and spectacles, but what the patient really needs is contact to keep him from feeling worthless and dependent. He likes to be kept up to date with current events and happenings and to be able to contribute to the goings on about him. The nurse, therefore, needs to take time to help him by, for example, reading to him and conversing if his sight is defective and by assisting his efforts to communicate should he be deaf. Small degress of deafness may go unnoticed, but sensitivity and perceptiveness will indicate the deficiency. It may well be necessary to use alternative forms of communication, eg visual messages and to indicate a sincere desire to help by direct physical contact such as a helping hand when his difficulty produces the inevitable frustration. Telling other patients of his deficit often helps them to communicate more easily with him.

Infirmity

Due to a variety of factors, the aged patient in hospitals is much more prone to accidents. This is mainly due to physical infirmity which prevents reactions which would enable the aged to take evasive action. With the previously mentioned sensory deficits and a tendency for aged patients to want to move about unaided at least some of the time, they are very prone to accidents involving falls and so on. Even then, a normal person might sustain minimal injury, but the aged to sustain, for example, fractured hips from trivial falls. Without seriously restricting the aged patient's movements, creating accident-free living situations within the ward is probably the only way in which such events might be eliminated. Infirmity, however, has an even more important aspect and one which, sadly enough, is often overlooked. This is the loss of dignity which may result when one becomes physically dependent upon others.

The aged patient suffers the effects of bed-rest more profoundly than a younger person and, as a result, their dependence is usually greater. A longer period of ambulation is required. The problem, therefore, is to give the required physical support whilst maintaining the patient's dignity and, at least, a degree of independence.

The aged person should be expected to carry out a certain amount of his own day-to-day care, and, although he may be assisted, activities such as washing should be left to him as far as possible. Initially, the patient may not like the situation but in the long run it will help him to retain his dignity and self respect. The point has already been made, but is worth repeating that patients are not merely clinical entities but people. Because they are people the implication is there that they have basic rights. These include the right to be as independent as possible to be called by their name and not by names such as 'pop' or 'dear'. They also have the right to be consulted about their treatment. A common mistake which nurses make with aged patients is to assume that physical infirmity creates or is accompanied by mental incapacity. This is seldom so outside of the psycho-geriatric ward and the burden of infirmity is greatly increased by being patronised or treated as a child. Worth remembering is the point that although the patient is physically disabled, given time and the right sort of assistance, he can accomplish a great deal more than the average nurse seems to appreciate.

Moods

Most of us are subject to changes in the way we react to situations, and these vary on a day-to-day basis. In the aged person there is often a marked resistance to change and this leads to irritability when change is thrust upon them. Fortunately, the mood changes to which the patient may be subject are easily changeable and sensitive understanding prevents much effort being expended in the long run.

All of us feel the need to be left alone sometimes. We feel we would like to be alone with our thoughts. A popular belief that aged people do not require moments of privacy is likely to lead to the patient getting annoyed. If the patient is meeting what is for him a life crisis we have no right to thrust pleasure upon him. In her daily interactions the nurse must appreciate the mood of the patient and act accordingly.

Institutionalization

Institutionalization is a phenomena which occurs in any situation where people live a communal type of existence. One of the most fertile places for its growth and development is the aged patient's hospital. This is not because becoming de-personalized and dependent upon the institution is a characteristic of old age, but because the will to resist the process as an individual requires so much energy that it may just not be available. Misplaced kindness accentuates the condition so that nurses who compel 'for their own good' aged patients to sit in 'baby-chairs' (chairs with front shelfs) or who make all the patient's decisions for him are really helping to develop this hospital-produced illness. The aged person has sensitivities just as acute and perceptive as a younger person and requires equal amounts of stimulation.

Institutionalization is characterized by lack of initiative, apathy, loss of contact with current events and activities. It sometimes produces a characteristic appearance with emotionless features not unlike those seen in depressive illnesses. The sufferer shows no interest in personal events and usually lacks those individual characteristics which differentiate one personality from another.

The solution is straightforward and simple and lies directly in the hands of those who manage and organize the patient's day. These are usually nurses of one sort or another.

The aged patient requires stimulation and contact from a variety of sources. He requires reminding of current and personal events and need the opportunity to keep personal possessions about him. Although contributing to the problem in the long run, a degree of directiveness is necessary initially and the inclusion of new activities and interests helps the situation considerably. It is worth stating that these patterns mentioned above are never solved by the switching on of a television set and leaving the aged parent in front of it.

Confusion

Confusion is a commonly encountered symptom in hospital which results from a variety of specific disease processes.

These include:

1 Infections
2 Intoxications (with drugs or alcohol)
3 Traumas
4 Circulatory disturbances
5 Metabolic disorders
6 Specific intra-cerebral diseases.

In old people confusion is basically one of perplexity, disorientation or varying degrees of clouding of consciousness. It produces, however, numerous 'psychological side effects' the management of which often falls upon a nurse in the course of her duties on the geriatric wards.

These include:

1 Emotional instability
2 Irritability
3 Inability to think or act quickly
4 Disorientation
5 Sensory dullness and misinterpretation
6 Obstinacy
7 Irritability
8 Fabrication

Generally the confused patient needs to be protected from common dangers that a reasonable person would avoid. The nurse requires to sort out which of the patients' symptoms are a result of his previous personality and which are due to confusion. For example, confused patients may be irritable but so might a normal individual with a low tolerance level in certain circumstances. The capacity of the confused patient varies so much that opportunity must be taken to achieve certain activities when he is not as confused. There should be a general avoidance of situations which 'upset' the patient and those procedures known to exacerbate his episodes should be avoided. (Some old people for example become confused when subject to hot baths; presumably due to vascular changes.)

Specific Nursing Points

1 A confused patient alternates between sweet reason and anger without the slightest provocations. Empathy enables the nurse to understand the reasons for this. The action most likely to help the situation is to accept the patient's behaviour without reaction.

2 Everyone is irritated and frustrated when those about him are unable to fulfil his needs and he is unable to communicate them. If a patient becomes irritable it is probably because some need is not being met and examination of the situation may reveal its nature, 'anticipation reduces frustration'.

3 There is little point in expecting the patient to understand and to act upon detailed instructions. The language used should be simple and precise. For example, a complex activity such as getting washed cannot be given as an instruction 'please have a wash'. It needs to be broken down into more simple phrases such as 'wash your hands please', 'now wash your face' and so on.

4 Because his appreciation of reality is disturbed, we must appeal to as many perceptual input channels as possible. The whole approach to the patient needs to be a multi-sensory one appealing to as many senses as is possible.

5 Confused patients may appear to be obstinate. This is because they dislike new activity or cannot generate the volition or understanding required to complete a task. The patient requires patience.

6 Fabrication is the invention of events which some patients exhibit during confusion to fill in gaps in their memory. It is often seen in the early days of degenerative cerebral disorders and may be an attempt to protect oneself psychologically. From a nursing point of view it is insignificant and should be ignored.

7 Confused old persons sometimes attempt to set out on imaginary (real to them) journeys or call the nurse by the name of a near relative of theirs. Observation prevents the occurrence

of accidents and understanding attention is probably a solution.

8 The speech of confused patients is frequently mixed up or nonsensical. Despite its obvious confusion, it may well seem quite alright to the patient and should not be a source of irritation to the nursing staff.

9 Finally, being disorientated and confused is a fear-creating situation even for the healthiest of us. The nurse must, therefore, be prepared to be with the patient even when he appears not to appreciate. A friendly firm hand may help to convey a message which cannot be communicated verbally. The patient will appreciate the attention.

9
Special Problems

All situations in hospitals are 'special' because they involve the feelings and sensitivities of human beings. This section of the book is intended to specifically mention some situations which are perhaps different from the bulk of the material so far expressed. These situations include:

Patients in the 'Medical' Wards
Patients in the 'Surgical' Wards
The Urological Patient
The Psychiatric Patient
The Dying Patient
Patients' Relatives

Patients in the Medical Ward

Medical illnesses as opposed to surgical conditions tend to be of longer duration. This results in a longer period of hospitalization for the medical patient.

Some medical conditions are so well talked about and discussed in the media, that no one suffering from them can be free of anxiety. The best example of this is heart disease. Heart attacks are of course frequently fatal. Almost none of us cannot recall an acquaintance or relative who has 'dropped dead' with what was believed to be such a condition. It is understandable that a patient on finding he has such a condition becomes acutely afraid that he will die. The usual manifestation of this situation is anxiety, but in some cases the patient's anxiety is such that he imposes an unnecessary life of an invalid upon himself for fear that exertion will result in his demise.

Other medical conditions, whilst not causing acute anxiety about the possibility of dying, suddenly so handicap the patient that his movement and activity is severely curtailed. Still other conditions produce symptoms which are distasteful to most human beings such as the expectorations of a chronic bronchitic. To be acceptable, most people concern themselves with their physical appearance. To be handicapped or physically unattractive is, therefore, psychologically damaging to most people.

The solutions to most of these problems are dealt with in other sections of the text. The boredom of a 'long-stay' patient will respond to general measures and opportunity whenever possible to make a positive contribution to the ward activities. Long-stay patients can, for example, serve a useful purpose in helping new patients settle in and are often asked to help look after other patients with problems such as a blind patient, eg taking him to the toilet or wash basin, or run a ward library service. In this way the patient's self-esteem and need for participation may be usefully fulfilled.

Anxiety due to any factor may be diminished by the measures suggested elsewhere in the text. One of the main problems on a medical (or indeed surgical) ward is the business of the unattractive patient. Few people, nurses included, are not influenced by physical appearance. Our whole culture set high store on acceptability in this sense. The initial approach to another individual is made easier and even desirable when they appear pleasant to look at. Patients with unpleasant symptoms, physical deformity or such conditions as skin diseases start with a handicap in as much as the nurse may be 'put off' by their appearance.

Physical appearance, as anyone who has enjoyed satisfactory relationships would confirm, is seldom an adequate basis if it is not supported by something else. Almost everyone is more attractive when one gets to know them. A few years ago the writer shared an office with an unattractive person (in a physical sense). The prospect of sharing with her did not seem on the surface too good an exercise yet, a few months later when the writer really got to know the person, she had so much more to offer in the way of gentleness and personality that her physical appearance became irrelevant.

What is implied is that a person who is physically repugnant is not necessarily unattractive. It is the nurse's task to raise the patient's self-esteem by interacting on a basis not built upon superficial factors. A patient's appearance may appear to himself so unfortunate that he cannot find the effort necessary to carry on. This condition may be transient, disappearing with the symptom or related to an uncorrectable situation such as the amputation of a limb. In all cases the measures undertaken to restore the patient's self-opinion are based upon the use of the nurse/patient relationship to fulfil his psychological needs.

One cannot develop a relationship if the components of understanding and mutual respect are not present. To get near to a patient in a psychological sense one must not be repelled by his appearance. The nurse's genuineness will be apparent to the patient in her tone of voice, her physical nearness, the topic of conversation, the amount of eye contact and her facial expression.

Superficial conversation which skirts around the problem will serve to reinforce the patient's lack of belief in himself. If one avoids physical contact with a patient when day to day activities in hospital necessitate it and, if she avoids the patient's eyes, the nurse expresses the fact that she is repelled by him. She also sets an example to other patients who watch the nurse's behaviour and often use it as a model for their own. In short, it is easily apparent to the patient when he is being rejected. The situation means that his needs of security and affection and acceptance are not met. His behaviour will indicate that this is so. The patient may become anxious, or may project his feelings and show aggressiveness. Most frequently the patient turns in on himself and is withdrawn and unhappy.

The approach to such a patient is essentially no different from any other and all measures which are undertaken with other patients should be operative with this patient. Activity and procedures should not make any difference of the patient's situation and because of the need of security, the nurse might make a point of really concentrating and these aspects above which characterise social contact.

There should be an effort to identify and exploit other aspects of the patient which will help to make him more acceptable to other patients.

The Patient in the Surgical Ward

Many years ago before the advent of anaesthesia and modern surgical techniques, a patient going to hospital for surgery must have done so with a great deal of apprehension and one suspects, only went if absolutely necessary. In the present days of sophisticated equipment and techniques nurses sometimes run the risk of forgetting about such factors as the patient's pre-operative anxieties.

To think about a surgeon carrying out some operation upon oneself is an unpleasant experience. To anticipate it is even worse. Nurses on surgical wards should, therefore, spend a great deal of their time 're-assuring' the patient about to have surgery.

Medical and nursing text books are full of the phrase 're-assure the patient'. In most cases this means to reduce the patient's anxiety. Anxiety prior to an operation is not only undesirable but it is also dangerous for extreme of anxiety prior to surgery accentuates the degree of post-operative shock. A drug given as pre-medication is no solution to the problem since the anxiety, although increasing as the event draws near, is present even days before. A friend once told the writer that he was going to have an operation to repair a hernia, but could not be operated on until September. He said that was alright because he would not need to start worrying until August, after his holiday! In the words of so many old films 'It's the waiting that is the worst'!!

To solve the problem and thereby find a solution, the nurse needs to examine the situation to ask certain questions and take the appropriate action.

She should ask:
Why does the patient feel anxiety?
Is this because he does not understand what is being done to him?
Does he lack confidence in the nursing staff, surgeons or both?
If so, why?
Is this related to previous experience or due to hearsay, rumour or merely lack of adequate information?

This leads on to such questions as whether the patient has been given adequate explanations about what is to be done, what is expected of him, whether there are symptoms to expect later?

These questions logically lead to the following actions:

The patient should be given adequate explanations about his surgery by the surgeon responsible.

His role in the procedure should be explained by the senior nurse responsible and, preferably, by a nurse with whom he is already familiar and trusts.

He should be encouraged to talk to other patients who have had similar operations successfully.

He should be told honestly what to expect later.

On the day of operation the patient's preparation should be casual with the nurse using her interpersonal skills to exhibit to the patient her genuine interest in him.

He should be taken to the theatre with a capable familiar nurse who should remain with him until he is anaesthetized.

Concern and the fulfilment of need may be achieved by touching the patient, eg by holding his hand during inducement of anaesthesia.

All other measures related to fulfilling needs of security should be given priority in the care of the patient. Support should be subject to be effective.

The Urological Patient

This section is included in the special problems because of the unique situation of the urological patient, both male and female.

The reproductive and urinary organs are different from other body systems in their effects upon the patient because they are associated with a great number of social restrictions. This is a result of the sexuality of human beings and the social and legal prohibitions thereby imposed upon the individual.

It is not socially acceptable to be 'exposed' to other people, yet on coming into hospital, the patient is subject to examination by a great number of persons. Needless to say, this results in considerable embarrassment for the patient and explains why many urological patients delay seeking medical treatment.

There is also a vague layman's idea that disorders of the kidneys and associated areas are almost always fatal. One reads daily of 'transplants' and 'artificial kidneys'.

The male patient in a urological ward (and to a lesser extent the female) is subject to a threat to his potency and fertility. Both of these are very important in the 'proof' of his masculinity. The age of the patient, of course, modifies the situation and one would anticipate a different reaction from a young unmarried man than an older man with a grown-up family. In all age groups the problem causes a lot of anxiety. The writer recalls a man of sixty years with a grown-up family having his prostrate gland removed and being told accidentally as it happened, by a nurse, that he was now sterile as a result. The man reacted with a great deal of anger at 'not being warned about it' beforehand. In reality the situation was not that straightforward since it is one thing for a consultant surgeon to tell the patient and another for a young (possibly inexperienced) nurse. His anger may well have been genuine or an attempt to conceal his 'loss of manhood' in the eyes of the young nurse.

The solution to the problem of embarrassment during

examinations and procedures usually rests with the nurse. Utmost privacy should be ensured during such activities and when discussion of the patient's problems is taking place care should be taken that it is private enough not to be overheard by other patients. When the necessity for intimate procedures arises they should be carried out by nurses of the same sex and the nurses should approach the patient in a casual matter-of-fact way to minimize his inevitable embarrassment.

The patient's fears about the nature of urinary disorders can usually be effectively allayed by sensible, simple explanation taking into account the patient's personality and maturity. It is always wise to leave the decision about how much information to impart to the medical staff involved. This does not necessarily mean absolution of the nurse from any responsibility.

For the problem of fears of potency and sterility account is to be taken of the patient's age, marital status and self-image of masculinity. It is usually reasonable to expect the medical staff to discuss the problems involved with the patient, but also to anticipate questions to the nursing staff. Answers to questions should follow the line dictated by the medical staff, but a patient getting his answer from a nurse with whom he has a good relationship is likely to be more reassured by the answer.

The Psychiatric Patient

The least understood and most maligned patient one encounters in a hospital ward is the patient suffering from mental illness.

Although there have been major advances in the conception and nature of mental disorder, there are still many persons, including many nurses, who have no experience of mental illness. This leads to the nurses acting according to the myths and misconceptions to which the psychiatric patient has fallen victim over the years.

Many lay people believe that the psychiatric patient, especially if he is not physically ill, has adopted this way of behaviour due to some motive of his own. It is implied, therefore, that since his behaviour is voluntary he must be able to do something about it when requested to do so. The writer does not intend to imply, nor does he believe, that psychiatric disorder cannot be corrected by reasoned judgment and a socialisation process, but rather that it is not merely a form of 'weakness' that makes the patient behave as he does.

In the lay person's concept of psychiatric illness, the patient is likely to behave in a most bizarre manner and to be immediately recognizable as a 'mad-man'. In reality most psychiatric disorders are little more than exaggerated reactions to which most people are subject, albeit to a lesser degree.

Some forms of mental illness are more profound, but even in these patients there is seldom the behaviour or threat as implied by the media when producing fiction involving mental disorder.

The psychiatric patient in a general ward will exhibit the types of behaviour described previously. It will be the same as the physically sick patient, but may occur more frequently.

In the more severe disorders the patient is likely to be withdrawn rather than active, quiet rather than noisy and fearful rather than threatening. The blind, deaf or lame do not necessarily suffer more than the mentally ill and many suffer infinitely less and yet are subject to much more sympathy.

The secret of success when dealing with psychiatric patients is to treat them as one would treat anyone else in a hospital ward. The psychiatric patient's needs are just as profound as their physically ill counterpart. His sensitivities are just as acute. Above all, the most important point to grasp is that his symptoms are involuntary and cannot be dismissed as deviant behaviour over which he has control.

Psychiatric disorder is basically divided into neurosis (emotional disorder) and psychosis (thinking disorder). The main component of a neurotic illness is a high anxiety factor and this can be dealt with just as previously indicated. Psychiatric disorders are generally speaking those disorders where the patient's cognitive processes are disordered. A psychotic patient may be *non compos mentis* or may not, depending on the severity. Patients who are psychotic may show behaviour which is inappropriate to the circumstance such as hallucinations or delusions. On the other hand, this does not mean the nurse should anticipate an abnormal response, but should act accordingly when such symptoms occur. It used to be an old maxim in psychiatric nursing that the nurse never agreed with or argued against delusional thinking. Current ideas suggest that she should constantly try to reinforce the patient's contact and appreciation of reality. Much of this involves the use of language and, if the patient's behaviour is disordered enough to cause an acute problem, the following points will help minimize the situation:

The nurse should define for the problem for the patient and say where he is and who she is, eg 'You are in hospital, Mr Smith. I am your nurse'. She should try to draw him away from exciting influences and demonstrate her concern: 'Come with me, Mr Smith, we will find a place where we can find out what is troubling you'.
Use the patient's name in a genuine manner – it helps define your personal interest.
Give opportunity for the patient to 'climb down' without loss of esteem.
We all dislike losing face.
Don't let situations influence your general relationship with the patient.

The real problem in nursing psychiatric patients is to get over to the patient that there is no need for overt forms of behaviour in order to draw attention to oneself or to have one's needs met. The only way that this method gets over is by giving the attention when the patient is not behaving in an overt manner. The nurse should endeavour to apply operant principles to the situation. Operant theory was described by B. F. Skinner and, basically, says that a response is likely to be repeated if it is rewarded immediately afterwards, ie the reward increases the frequency of the response. Principles based upon operant theory might therefore include:

Ignore completely inappropriate behaviour since any reference to it will serve to reinforce it and increase its frequency

Give the patient attention when his behaviour is normal (ie socially acceptable) thus increasing the frequency of *this* behaviour

Give verbal praise, but not over effusively, at the time of achievement

Do not anticipate abnormal behaviour. A 'sick' patient will act like a sick patient

If the patient's behaviour becomes inappropriate, it is best to take him to a quiet place to recover. This is comparable to a pigeon in 'Skinner Box' having its light switched out when it became erratic.

The Dying Patient

Asked which aspect of the nurses' work they feel most anxious about, a young nurse entering the profession usually says caring for the dying patient. Coping with the dying patient *is* a disturbing problem and one which is regrettably encountered frequently.

There have been many excellent accounts of the psychological aspects of dying. Notable amongst the writers and workers is Elizabeth Kubler-Ross to whose book the reader is referred. The problem is dealt with here since it is such an important task that it cannot be left out.

There is no analogy in life which could reasonably be compared with the experience of dying. Even the bereavement of a near relative, although grieving and disturbing, cannot be compared with it.

The fact is that a patient who is dying is about to be separated from everyone and everything which he holds dear. There can be no fulfilment of any sort after the event. There is the worry of who will care for those left behind and whether adequate provision has been made for them.

In hospital the problem does not seem too large to a member of the nursing staff. This is because people in all caring situations tend to become blunted and erect a facade of apparent indifference. When confronted with an unpleasant situation such as this there are three usual ways of behaving. One can use unhealthy mechanisms, eg one can 'deny' that it is so. The situation can be 'avoided', ie the individuals involved can withdraw as far as possible from the anxiety provoking stimulus or finally one can face the reality and try to come to terms with it.

In hospital the usual way is to 'deny' the situation or to avoid it. Denial is used in two ways. The medical and nursing staff may fail to tell the patient that his demise is near. In these cases withdrawal (avoidance) usually accompanies the falsehood since it is easier to avoid a patient than answer unanswerable questions. The second way it is used is to tell the patient that he is dying, await his psychological denial (a natural reaction) and then encourage it by offering glimmers of false hope.

Whether or not to tell a patient that he is dying is usually a policy decision decided by the medical staff. In the writer's opinion there are few justifications for withholding the truth notwithstanding the protection of patient or relative. If the patient is not told, not only do we deceive him, but we prevent him from having the opportunity to put his affairs in order before his death. What is questionable about whether to tell or not to tell the patient is the motive involved. Can we be sure that withholding the truth is best for him as well as *us*. Interacting with a dying patient is not easy. There are many factors which make the patient difficult. One of the main ones is communication.

In the general course of a nurse's work she exchanges social chit chat with her patients. She talks about the next holiday, about last night's film, about the fact of spring emerging or sometimes about those about her. All this takes place in a fairly light-hearted casual way without being too involved in the patient's problem.

What does one say to a dying patient? Talk about the future is inappropriate, the past saddening, and the present anxiety-provoking. A usual reaction is therefore to talk only if absolutely necessary and even simpler to deny that such a situation ever exists.

The writer has been told by patients in hospital of the indications which signal to them that a particular patient is dying. Being moved to a private area of the ward away from the main activity; being missed out on the consultant's round; relatives visiting without restrictions. In short, although we may not tell a patient that he is dying, the way we react to him tells him and others. We unconsciously withdraw. Sadly though, the work of Elizabeth Kubler-Ross has indicated that most of all the dying patient does not want to be left alone or excluded from the course of events. Such a situation only adds to his burden.

The writer once encountered a patient who knew he was dying, but was encouraged to deny the fact by those involved in his care. He had already come to terms with his situation, but to help the nurses survive the anxiety of being with him he pretended he knew nothing of it. One cannot but guess what he was feeling in such a situation, but to have to pretend in such a way must have been a great strain.

Generally speaking a patient who is dying goes through several 'stages' before he finally, if ever, comes to terms with the predicament.

These are:

Denial	— the patient is unable to accept the situation consciously and refuses to believe it
Acceptance with Anger	— the patient accepts the situation, but is angry at being 'chosen' and he projects his anger on the staff and the hospital generally
Acceptance with Depression	— the patient accepts the situation and goes through a period of grieving. This is something akin to 'mourning in anticipation'
Bargaining — (as described by E. Kubler-Ross)	
	— the patient bargains for more time, perhaps to do, feel or see something or someone once more. The bargain may be made with the medical staff 'keep me going another week' but more usually with God
Resignation and peace	— a stage which seems to be only reached by a few patients. Perhaps because of the way we treat them.

A patient may not necessarily pass through all these stages and many patients die still denying their death. One is more likely to encounter all stages when a patient has been told he is going to die.

The nurse's duties in the psychological care of the dying patient are quite clear. She is required to meet whatever 'need' the patient has at any stage of the process.

She does not help the situation by encouraging the mechanism of dying and one should be aware of the foregone comments. When the patient is angry at the fact of his death and becomes irritated with the nursing staff, she should accept the situation with equanimity and hostility on her part only creates a worse situation. She should empathise and thereby understand how the patient is feeling.

During the time that the patient is experiencing his great sadness the nurse should avoid overexhuberance and the high spirits of youth. She should be available to support the patient with a firm hand and an understanding voice. There should be no statements which are made to save the nurse embarrassment or effort such as 'act like an adult' or 'pull yourself together'.

If the patient bargains, it is by way of a last request. It should whenever reasonably possible be fulfilled for him. Access to relatives and any restrictions previously imposed might be lifted to make the patient's last hours as pleasant as is possible. Many patients who are dying require the services of the clergy and all such considerations should be fulfilled.

The nurse's reaction to her patient dying is also a specific one. Each patient who dies is in some way a 'failure' since the recovery of health is usually the primary function of hospitalization.

It may appear melodramatic to suggest that this is so, but each nurse unconsciously acknowledges failure when a patient dies. This is one of the reasons why the 'blunting effect' occurs, in order to prevent conscious acknowledgement of the fact.

Each time a patient dies the nurse is reminded of her own mortality and of that of her close friends and relatives. There is a process of identification going on which creates anxiety. This fact might be illustrated by observing the reactions of individuals in certain situations. A nurse (or indeed anyone) would be disturbed at the death of a young child. She would be even more disturbed if she had children of her own.

To be aware of the situation and to understand what is happening to her is half the solution.

Older members of the staff should help junior, younger members to deal with the situation both from their side and that of the patient.

The Care of the Dying Patient is most excellently described in the Parent Book of this series.

Relatives

From the point of view of the nurse, patient's relatives are almost as big a problem as some of her patients.

Relatives of patients are directly concerned in the patient's illness and implications resulting from it affect them fare more than the nurse. Patient's relatives also have a direct effect upon the emotional ease (or lack of it) of the patient since they are themselves emotionally tied to the patient. The patient's hospitalization may create for the relatives difficulties it is scarcely possible for a nurse to conceive. Imagine the effect upon a family if the mother is hospitalized and the father perhaps left with a young family to care for. Or the results of an old man and wife being separated when their only barrier against loneliness is each other.

When a patient is admitted to hospital relatives may feel relieved because help is to hand and their loved one is 'in the best place'. Alternatively, they may feel guilty about their relative having to go to hospital (parents of young children especially) feeling that they have failed them in some way, or that their neglect has resulted in the illness. These feelings are not usually conscious but they may be projected on to members of the hospital staff or the individual may use the hospital generally as the tangible target for their feelings of inadequacy. Which ever way a patient's relatives react, their reactions affect the emotional state of the patient and thereby the illness. The way in which a patient's relatives approach members of the nursing staff will probably colour the nurse's response to the patient. This, of course, indicates that nurses are no more immune from personal feelings than are other individuals.

Patients' relatives seldom understand the nature and meaning of the patient's illness and are further confused by the use of medical gargon and the air of mystery which members of the medical and nursing professions like to surround themselves. The relatives do not appreciate their behaviour in the total situation and, therefore, do little to help any difficulties that occur. Relatives of patients may ask questions that the staff cannot answer because they are really suggesting that the care of their loved one is inadequate.

It is easy for a nurse to react to the hostility of relatives, whether consciously or unconsciously with equal vindictiveness and lack of understanding. The nurse must see herself as a buffer between the patient and his relatives. She must protect the patient from the relative's symptoms! She must understand that to entrust someone whom you love dearly to the care of total strangers is difficult.

A good start to the problem of patient's relatives is to see that their concern for the patient is acknowledged by the staff and that adequate information is to hand at the outset.

The general approach should be as follows:

Understand the relatives' feelings and anxieties and help them to cope with them in a healthy way

Provide information at the time of admission in the form of a booklet or whatever. This should explain the position of the relative in the patient's illness and provide information with regard to hospital routines, facilities and regulations

Avoid the use of medical jargon when giving explanations and remember that it is very easy for someone who is upset to misinterpret what is being said to them

Accept from relatives behaviour which seems to be personal. They are projecting unpleasant emotional feelings. One should help rather than react

Be especially aware of relatives' feelings when the patient is a child or seriously ill

Create a situation wherein the individual feels confident in leaving his relatives in your care. It is usually obvious when concern which is expressed is genuine.

10
Dealing with Questions

The following quotation is from a medical journal and was authentic!

> *Patient: I'm having an IVP tomorrow, nurse. What is it?*
> *Nurse: An X-ray of your kidneys, I think.*
> *Patient: So I hear. But what happens to me?*
> *Nurse: Search me — I've never seen one.*

Smile first — then consider!

How Would You Deal with These?

1 A patient in a medical ward has had a heart attack and asks you whether he will be an invalid as a result

2 A young mother is suspected of having a malformed baby. She asks whether her baby will be alright

3 A patient tells you he feels hopeless and asks what reason he has for going on living

4 A patient is anxious about his forthcoming surgery and asks you whether he will be alright

5 Peter, a three-year-old infant, recently admitted to hospital asks when his mummy is coming back
or
why he cannot go home

7 A junior nurse asks how she should go about learning to form relationships with her patients

8 A patient of mature years asks you a question about his illness. He is going to die in the near future

9 A patient's relative asks you whether her daughter is getting the best care

10 A patient refuses to co-operate in his preparation for surgery

11 A male patient acts immodestly whenever he is given attention by a female nurse

12 An adolescent patient is noisy and annoys old patients

13 A female patient is worried about her family whilst she is in hospital

14 An elderly patient is too confused to follow instructions

15 A family is involved in a car crash. One killed, one seriously injured, two shocked

16 The relatives of a patient are in a country where there has been political upheaval, earthquake, hurricane etc

17 The patient is a close relative of one of your friends or neighbours

18 Why did my mummy not keep me at home in my own bed?

19 You know a patient on a controlled diet is getting unallowed food from visitors

20 An elderly patient gives nurse a watch or some other personal possession as a present.

Individual nurses apart — each of these topics would provide an excellent discussion point at tutorial level.

Keep a note of any others you may come across. They happen often.

11
Further Reading

Students who wish to expand their knowledge of matters referred to in the text may do so by reference to the following books:

1	Argyle, Michael	The psychology of Interpersonal Behaviour Penguin 02.08534
2	Eysenck, H. J.	Fact and Fiction in Psychology Penguin 02.0656.6
3	Eysenck, H. J.	Uses and Abuses of Psychology Penguin 02.02.81.7
4	Eysenck, H. J.	Sense and Nonsense in Psychology Penguin 02.0385.0
5	Illingworth, R. S.	The Development of the Infant and Young Child 4th Edit: Livingstone, Edin. 1972
6	Lee, E. A. & Sclare, A. B.	Psychiatry Heinemann. Modern Practical Nursing Series Vol. 7
7	McGee, Andrew	Psychology as Applied to Nursing 4th Edit: Livingstone, 1966
8	Primrose, David	Mental Deficiency Heinemann. Modern Practical Nursing Series
9	Robertson, James	Young Children in Hospital Tavistock, 1970
10	Seager, C. P.	Psychiatry for Nurses, Social Workers and Occupational Therapists Heinemann, 1968.

Index